COORDINATE GRAPHS

PETER ROBSON

 Newby Books

PO Box 40, Scarborough
North Yorkshire, YO12 5TW

COORDINATES

Coordinates show the position of a point. They are like map references.

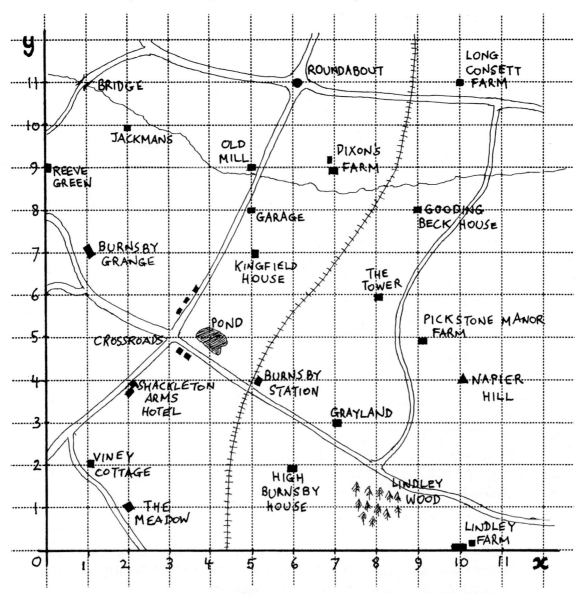

The straight line along the bottom is the **x axis** (horizontal axis).

The straight line up the left-hand side is the **y axis** (vertical axis).

The point where the x axis and y axis meet (or intersect) is the **ORIGIN.**

Each line along the x axis and y axis is numbered, starting with 0 at the bottom left-hand corner.

In the plan above, the coordinates of BURNSBY STATION are (5,4). To find the position of the station, count from the origin (0,0) along (in the x direction) 5 units and up (in the y direction) 4 units.

5 is the x coordinate and 4 is the y coordinate.

Coordinates are always written with the x (along) coordinate first ('Along the corridor and up the stairs!') - NEVER THE OTHER WAY ROUND. They are written inside brackets, and there is a comma between the x coordinate and the y coordinate.

Examples. The coordinates of Dixon's Farm are (7,9) and the coordinates of The Tower are (8,6) etc.

Things which lie on an axis have a zero (0) coordinate, e.g. Lindley Farm (10,0).

To answer **1**, **2**, **3** and **4** look at the plan on page 2.

1 What things or places can you find at these coordinates?
(a)	(2,10)	(e)	(6,11)	(i)	(7,3)		
(b)	(6,2)	(f)	(5,8)	(j)	(5,7)		
(c)	(8,6)	(g)	(8,1)				
(d)	(1,2)	(h)	(10,11)				

2 What are the coordinates of these? Copy the names and write the correct coordinates next to each name. Remember to put the commas and brackets.

The Meadow	Shackleton Arms Hotel
Gooding Beck House	Old Mill
Burnsby Grange	Pickstone Manor Farm
Napier Hill	Bridge
Pond	Reeve Green

3 Write down the coordinates of the point which is exactly HALFWAY between
(a)   Dixon's Farm and Grayland
(b)   Shackleton Arms Hotel and The Tower
(c)   Garage and Gooding Beck House
(d)   Long Consett Farm and The Meadow
(e)   Reeve Green and Long Consett Farm

4 What other place (or places) would an aircraft pass over if it flew in a straight line from
(a)   Viney Cottage to Bridge
(b)   The Meadow to Gooding Beck House
(c)   Long Consett Farm to Bridge
(d)   Lindley Farm to Dixon's Farm
(e)   Old Mill to Napier Hill

5 (a)   On squared paper, draw an x axis and a y axis like the ones on page 2. Number the axes correctly, starting at 0 and remembering that the numbers go on the lines (not in the spaces).
(b)   Using these axes, draw your own invented plan of a village, town, island or anything sensible. Mark and name TEN different things or places in your plan.
(c)   Write a list of the ten different things or places. Sort them into alphabetical order (Things beginning with A first, B next, C next, etc.). Then, against each thing or place in your list, write its coordinates. Remember the commas and brackets.

HOW TO PLOT POINTS

To plot a point, mark it in the correct position (ALONG first) with a dot.
Then draw a small circle round the dot to show where it is.

The diagram shows points
A   (2,1)
B   (8,3)
C   (7,6)
D   (1,4)

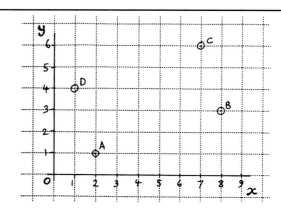

If you are asked to join two points, this should be done with a straight line, e.g. Join AB, BC, CD and DA to form a rectangle.

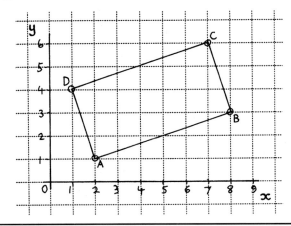

6 (a) Draw x and y axes from 0 to 9 each. Remember to number the <u>lines</u> ALONG the x axis from 0, and UP the y axis from 0.

(b) Plot points A (3,3), B (6,6), C (3,9), D (0,6). Join AB, BC, CD, DA to form a quadrilateral (four-sided figure). Write inside the quadrilateral which special kind it is.

(c) Plot points E (9,4), F (9,6), G (6,9), H (6,7). Join EF, FG, GH, HE to form a quadrilateral. Write inside the quadrilateral which special kind it is.

(d) Plot points J (6,5), K (8,4), L (6,0), M (4,1). Join to form a quadrilateral and write inside it which special kind it is.

(e) Write down the lengths, in units, of each of these
(Example. JL. Distance from J to L is 5 units. Length of JL is 5.)
(i) AC, (ii) BF, (iii) GJ, (iv) FD, (v) JC.

7 (a) Draw x and y axes from 0 to 9 each.

(b) Plot points A (0,6), B (2,6), C (2,7), D (3,0), E (9,9), F (6,6), G (2,4), H (8,0), I (8,8), J (5,6), K (5,4), L (4,5), M (9,7), N (8,5), P (8,6), Q (4,9), R (3,5), S (9,4), T (6,4), U (3,6), V (7,9), W (8,9), X (4,6), Y (7,5), Z (7,6).

(c) Join QV, WE, CM, AB, UX, JF, ZP, RL, YN, GS, GC, RU, LX, KJ, TF, YZ, NP, IW, SE, CQ, KD, MV, HT to make a picture.

Positive (+) and negative (−) coordinates

The origin (0,0) is often drawn in the centre of the diagram to show positive (+) and NEGATIVE (−) values on the x and y axes.

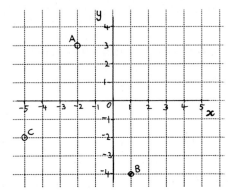

In this diagram, the coordinates of A are (−2,3). To find the position of A, count from the origin along (in the x direction) −2 units and up (in the y direction) 3 units.

The coordinates of B are (1,−4); the coordinates of C are (−5, −2).

8 This is a rough plan of Alton Towers Theme Park in Staffordshire. On this plan, the origin (0,0) has been drawn roughly in the centre, giving positive (+) and negative (–) axes.

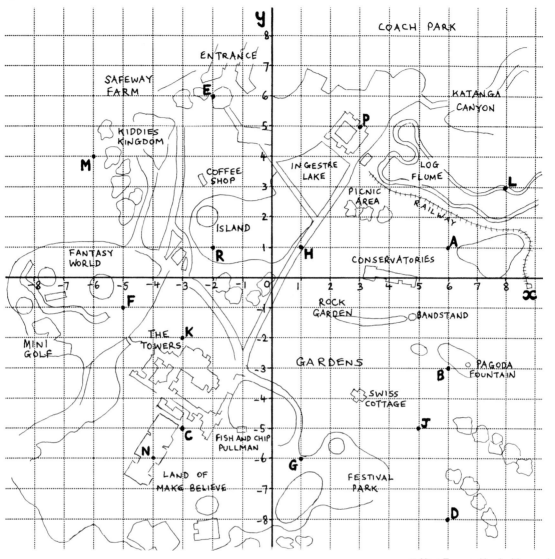

© Alton Towers. Used with permission.

The coordinates of Safeway Farm are (–5,6). Count –5 on the x axis and +6 on the y axis.

The coordinates of Swiss Cottage are (3,–4). Count +3 on the x axis and –4 on the y axis.

The coordinates of Fish and Chip Pullman are (–1,–5). Count –1 on the x axis and –5 on the y axis.

On the plan of Alton Towers, what features (things) can you find at each of these?

(a)	(3,2)	(e)	(–3,–7)	(i)	(–8,–2)
(b)	(7,6)	(f)	(–1,7)	(j)	(5,8)
(c)	(–4,4)	(g)	(4,0)		
(d)	(7,–3)	(h)	(3,–7)		

9 Andrew (A), Brenda (B), Carrie (C), David (D), Emma (E), Frances (F), George (G), Helen (H), Jamil (J), Karen (K), Lee (L), Mohammed (M), Nelson (N), Patrick (P) and Ruth (R) are visiting Alton Towers. Their positions are marked on the plan above. Write the name of each person and his/her coordinates.

10 The diagram shows the rough positions of a fielding cricket team. The coordinates of the batsman are (2,0). Make a list of the names and write the correct coordinates against each name.

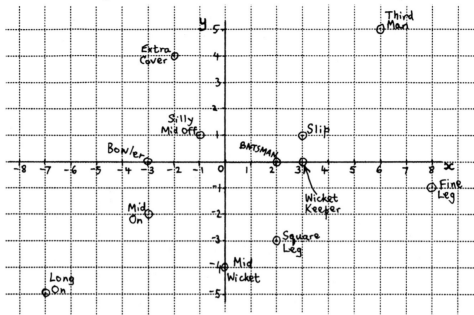

Remember which signs fit which regions.

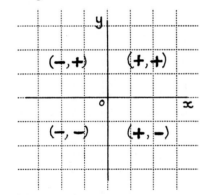

When you are drawing axes, make quite sure that –1 on the y axis is numbered correctly (It is the next line below the x axis.).

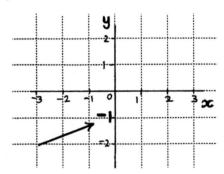

11 (a) Draw x and y axes from –5 to +5 each, with the origin (0,0) in the centre.
(b) Plot points A (5,0), B (–1,3), C (2,–3), D (5,–3). Join AB, BC, CD, DA to form a quadrilateral. Write inside the quadrilateral which special kind it is.
(c) Repeat (b), but instead of ABCD, plot and join E (1,4), F (–2,3), G (–5,4), H (–2,5). Write which special kind of quadrilateral you have drawn.
(d) Repeat (b) again, but instead of ABCD, plot and join P(1,–3), Q (–3,1), R (–5, –2), S (–2, –5). Write which special kind of quadrilateral it is.

12 (a) Draw x and y axes from –10 to +10. Plot these points:–
A (–6,0), B (–7, –1), C (–8, –1), D (–6, 1), E (–7,3), F (–9,6), G (–10,9), H (–7,6), J (–9,9), K (–7,8), L (–4,4), O (0,0), M (4,–6), N (7,–8), P (9,–8), Q (5,–9), R (2,–8), S (2,–10), T (0,–10), U (1,–8), V (–2,–5), W (–2,–7), X (–4,–10), Y (–6,–10), Z (–4,–8), AA (–4,–6), BB (–5,–1), CC (–6,–2), DD (–7,–2), EE (–5,0).
(b) Join the points in the <u>same order</u> as shown above (AB, BC, CD, etc.) with straight lines to make a graphosaurus (a new kind of tyrannosaurus).
(c) Complete the graphosaurus by plotting point I (–6½, 6½). Draw a ring round the point.

STRAIGHT-LINE GRAPHS

VERTICAL AND HORIZONTAL GRAPHS

If, for example, the points (4,1), (4,4) and (4,–3) are joined, the result is a vertical straight line. This line is the GRAPH of x=4 because all points on the line have an x coordinate of 4.

The EQUATION of the graph is x=4.

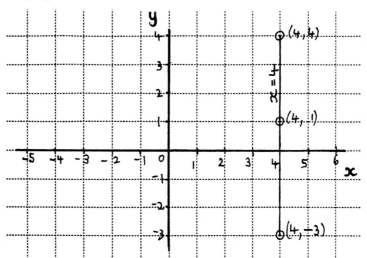

Other similar graphs can be drawn in a similar way, e.g.

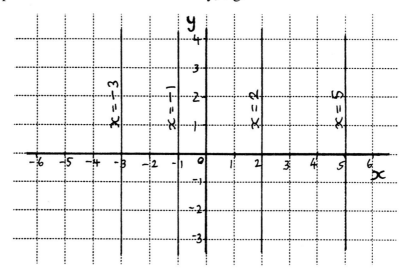

A straight line graph goes on for ever in both directions. When you are drawing a straight line graph, always produce (extend) it as far as you can in both directions.

NOTE. The graph of x=0 is the same line as the y axis.

13 (a) Draw x and y axes with the origin in the centre.

(b) Plot points (3,5), (3,0), (3,–4). Join the points with a line and produce the line as far as you can in both directions. Label the line (write next to it) x=3.

(c) Plot points (6,2), (6,4), (6,–3). Join to make a straight line graph. Label the graph with the correct equation.

(d) Plot (–4,0), (–4,4), (–4,–5). Draw a straight line graph through these points and label the graph with the correct equation.

(e) Using the same axes, draw and label the graphs of x=1 and x=–2. All the graphs you have drawn should be PARALLEL.

If, for example, the points (4,3), (1,3), (–2,3) and (–5,3) are joined, the result is a horizontal straight line. This is the graph of y=3 because all the points on the line have a y coordinate of 3.

The EQUATION of the graph is y=3.

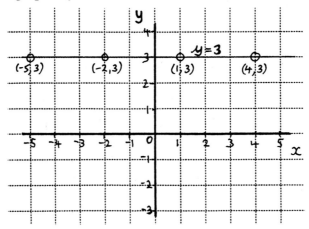

Other similar graphs can be drawn in a similar way, e.g.

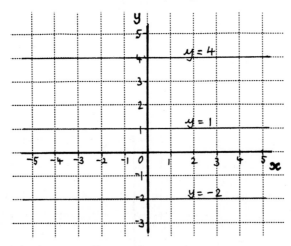

NOTE. The graph of y=0 is the same line as the x axis.

Points of intersection
The point of intersection of two graphs is the point where the two graphs meet or cross, e.g.

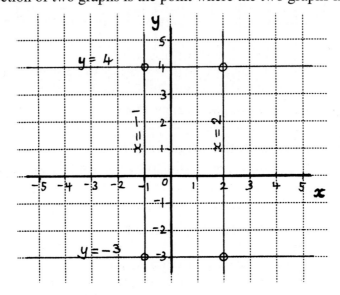

The point (–1,4) is the intersection of the graphs x= –1 and y=4. The point (2,4) is the intersection of the graphs x=2 and y=4. Which graphs intersect at (–1,–3) and (2,–3)?

14
(a)   Draw x and y axes with the origin in the centre.
(b)   Plot points (0,2), (5,2), (–4,2). Join the points and produce the line in both directions. Label the line y=2.
(c)   Plot points (1,–4), (4,–4), (–5,–4). Draw a straight line graph through these points and label the graph with the correct equation.
(d)   Using the same axes, draw the graph of x=4.
(e)   What are the coordinates of the point of intersection of x=4 and y=2?
(f)   Using the same axes, draw the graphs of
      (i) x=–2,   (ii) y=5,   (iii) x=1,   (iv) y=–2

15   This is a simplified street plan of part of San Francisco (U.S.A.). On this plan the streets have been numbered –5 to +5 on the x and y axes. Each street represents a graph, e.g. Larkin Street is x=5, Bush Street is y=–4, etc. The intersection of Buchanan Street and Broadway is (–2,4), etc.

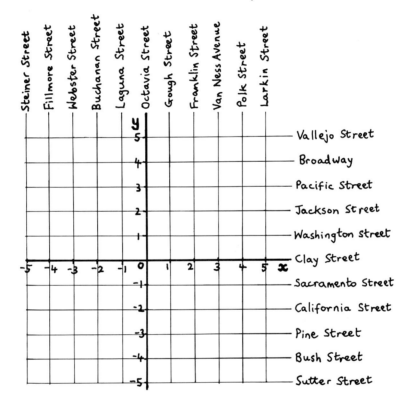

From the plan above write down the graph of
(a) Polk Street, (b), Washington Street, (c) Fillmore Street, (d) California Street, (e) Clay Street.
Which street has each of these graphs?
(f) x=3,   (g) x=–1,   (h) y=4,   (i) x=0,   (j) y=–4

16
(a)   Gough Street and Bush Street
(b)   Fillmore Street and Jackson Street
(c)   Van Ness Avenue and Clay Street
(d)   Polk Street and Broadway
(e)   Steiner Street and California Street

From the plan above, find the coordinates of intersection of

Write down which streets intersect at each of these points
(f) (–1,–1),   (g) (0,–5),   (h) (–3,3),   (i) (2,–1),   (j) (5,5)

Graphs of y=x, y=–x

In the coordinates (3,3), (1,1), (0,0), (–4,–4), etc., the x coordinate is always the same as (or equal to) the y coordinate. If these coordinates are joined, the line is the **graph of y=x.**

The equation is usually written with the y first, y=x (not usually x=y).

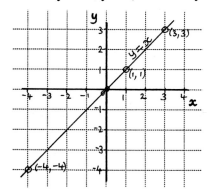

If, in the coordinates, the number values are the same, but one is positive (+) and the other negative (–), the points join up to form the **graph of y=–x,** e.g. coordinates (4,–4), (2,–2), (–1,1), (–3,3).

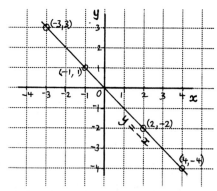

The graph of y=–x is sometimes called the graph of x+y=0.
The graphs of y=x and y=–x both pass through the origin (0,0).

---

17 (a) Plot points A (4,5), B (4,4), C (4, –1), D (4,–4), E (–3,–3), F (–3,–1),
G (–3,3), H (–5,5).
(b) Join AD, DH, AH, BE, CF and EG.
(c) AD is part of the graph of x=4. Copy and complete :–
EG is part of the graph of ...
AH is part of the graph of ...
CF is part of the graph of ...
BE is part of the graph of ...
DH is part of the graph of ...

---

18 (a) Draw x and y axes with the origin in the centre. Mark the origin O and plot
point A (0,6).
(b) OA is one of the diagonals of a square. Draw the other diagonal, marking
the ends of the diagonal B (3,3) and C.
(c) Join A, B, O and C to make the square. Copy and complete:–
OA is part of the graph of ...
OB is part of the graph of ...
CB is part of the graph of ...
OC is part of the graph of ...
(d) Work out the area of square ABOC in square units.

The y=x family of graphs

How to draw the graph of y=x

1) Choose any number for x, e.g.3

When x=3, y=3 because y=x. This gives the point (3,3).

2) Choose another value for x, e.g. −4

When x=−4, y=−4 because y=x. This gives the point (−4,−4)

3) Draw the graph by joining these points and producing the line.

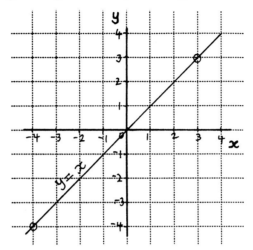

How to draw other graphs in the y=x family, e.g. y=x+2

1) Choose any number for x, e.g. 1

When x=1, y=1+2=3 because y=x+2. This gives the point (1,3).

2) Choose another number for x, e.g. −3

When x=−3, y=−3+2 = −1 because y=x+2. This gives the point (−3,−1).

3) Draw the graph by joining these points and producing the line.

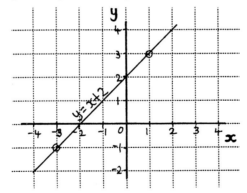

Graphs with equations beginning y=x all slope the same way and the same amount (they have the same GRADIENT) and so they are parallel.

Here are some more members of the y=x family.

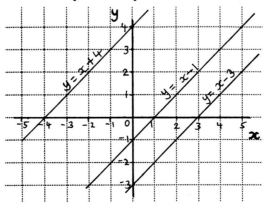

19 (a)   Draw x and y axes from –6 to +6.
(b)   Plot A (0,6), B (3,6), C (5,6), D (6,6), E (6,4), F (6,3), G (6,1), H (–6,0), J (–6,–3), K (–6,–5), L (–6,–6), M (–4,–6), N (–3,–6), P (–1,–6). In the top left-hand corner, draw an arrow pointing to the top of the page to show North.

(c)   A railway with two tracks runs from the South-West to the North-East. The rails of one track are KC and LD. The rails of the other track are ME and NF. Draw these and mark each line with its equation y=......

(d)   A road runs parallel to the railway. The two sides of the road are HA and JB. Draw these and mark each line with its equation.

(e)   A telephone line runs parallel to the railway from P to G. Join PG and mark with its equation.

---

20 All on the same axes, draw the graphs of
$$y=x$$
$$y=x+1$$
$$y=x-2$$
$$y=x+5$$
$$y=x-4$$

The y=2x family of graphs

y=2x

e.g.   When x=0, y=2 x 0= 0, giving point (0,0)
When x=1, y=2 x 1=2, giving point (1,2)
When x=2, y=2 x 2=4, giving point (2,4)
When x=–2, y=2 x –2=–4, giving point (–2,–4)

These points, when joined, give the graph of y=2x

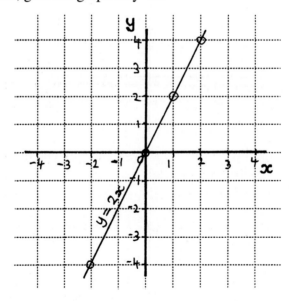

The graph of y=2x is twice the steepness of the graph of y=x (It has 2 times the gradient).

To draw other graphs in the y=2x family, e.g. y=2x+1, choose any values of x, e.g. 2 and –1

When x=2, y= 2x2 +1 = 5, giving the point (2,5).
When x=–1, y= 2x–1 +1 = –2 +1 = –1, giving the point (–1,–1).

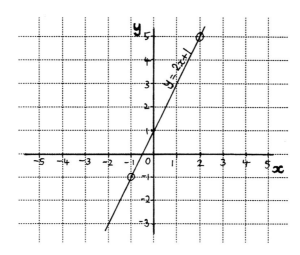

Graphs with equations beginning y=2x all slope the same way and the same amount (they have the same gradient) so they are parallel.

21 All on the same axes, draw the graphs of
y=2x, y=2x+3, y=2x–2, y=2x–1, y=2x+2
Mark each graph with its correct equation.

22 (a)   Draw x and y axes from –6 to +6. Draw the graph of x=2. Pretend this graph is a wall. Draw the graph of y=–4. Pretend this graph is the ground.

(b)   Plot J (–6,–4), K (–4,–4), L (–3,–4), M (–2,–4), N (–1,–4), P (2,6), Q (2,4), R (2,2)

(c)   PL, JQ, KR, MQ and NR are all ladders leaning against the wall. Draw each ladder. Then copy and complete :–

The equation of PL is ......
The equation of JQ is ......
The equation of KR is ......
The equation of MQ is ......
The equation of NR is ......

(d)   The coordinates of S are (0,–2). What special kind of quadrilateral is OMSR ?

Drawing straight–line graphs

Any straight line graph (like the y=x and y=2x families) can be drawn by finding two points on the graph and joining them. It is safer to draw three points in case you have made a mistake with one of the others.

e.g. Draw the graph of y=3x–5.

Choose three values for x, e.g. 0, 1, 2.
When x=0, y= (3×0)–5 = –5,
                        giving point (0,–5)
When x=1, y= (3×1)–5 = –2,
                        giving point (1,–2)
When x=2, y= (3×2)–5 = 1,
                        giving point (2,1)
By joining these points, the graph
        of y=3x–5 can be drawn.

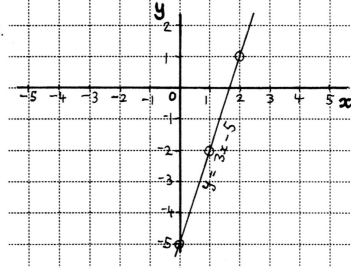

23 Draw these graphs by choosing values of x

(a) $y = x - 3$ (f) $y = x + 6$

(b) $y = 3x + 1$ (g) $y = 3 - 3x$

(c) $y = 2x - 4$ (h) $y = 2x + 7$

(d) $y = 4 - x$ (i) $y = \frac{1}{3}x + 1$

(e) $y = \frac{1}{2}x + 2$ (j) $y = -2x - 4$

Another way to draw straight line graphs

Find the value of y when x = 0

the value of x when y = 0

e.g. Draw the graph of $y = 2x + 6$

$\underline{\text{When } x = 0}$ $y = 2x + 6$

$y = (2 \times 0) + 6$

$y = 6$ giving the point (0,6)

$\underline{\text{When } y = 0}$ $0 = 2x + 6$

$-6 = 2x$

$-3 = x$ giving the point (−3,0)

By joining these points, the graph of $y = 2x + 6$ can be drawn.

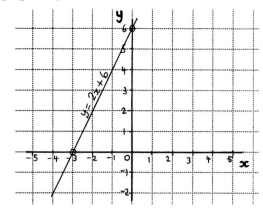

e.g. (2)   Draw the graph of $2y = 8 - x$

When x = 0, y = 4   giving the point (0,4)

When y = 0, x = 8   giving the point (8,0)

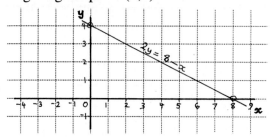

24 For each of these equations, find

(i)   the value of y when x = 0

(ii)   the value of x when y = 0

Using these values, draw the graph of each equation

(a) $y = 2x - 7$ (f) $x + y = 6$

(b) $2x + y = 3$ (g) $2y - x = 3$

(c) $2y - 3x = 12$ (h) $y + 5x = -5$

(d) $y = \frac{1}{2}x - 3$ (i) $2y - 2x = 9$

(e) $y = 5x + 5$ (j) $y = 8 - 4x$

GRADIENT

Gradient means 'steepness'. It is the VERTICAL DISTANCE (distance up) divided by the HORIZONTAL DISTANCE (distance along), e.g.

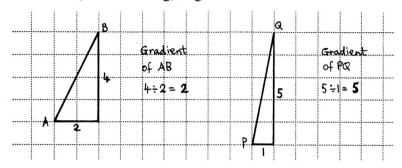

Road gradients (in the U.K.) are signposted either as ratios or percentages, e.g.

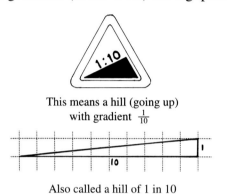

This means a hill (going up)
with gradient $\frac{1}{10}$

Also called a hill of 1 in 10

This means a hill (going up)
with gradient $\frac{25}{100} = \frac{1}{4}$

Also called a hill of 1 in 4

Railway gradients in the U.K. are never as steep as the steepest road gradients. The best-known gradient on British Rail, and the longest steep gradient on a main high-speed line (the Lickey incline near Bromsgrove on the line between Birmingham and Bristol) is $\frac{1}{37}$.

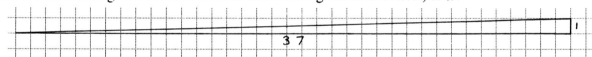

Cable-car railways and rack-and-pinion railways are sometimes as steep as $\frac{1}{2}$.

Anything which slopes has a gradient, e.g.

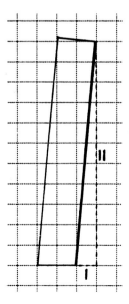

The Leaning Tower of Pisa (Italy) has a gradient of about 11

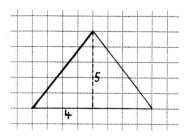

The sloping side of the Great Pyramid of King Khufu (Egypt) has a gradient of about
$\frac{5}{4} = 1\frac{1}{4}$

25 Measure the vertical distance (up) and the horizontal distance (along) in each of these. Then find the gradient of each by calculating

$$\frac{\text{vertical distance}}{\text{horizontal distance}}$$ (or vertical ÷ horizontal)

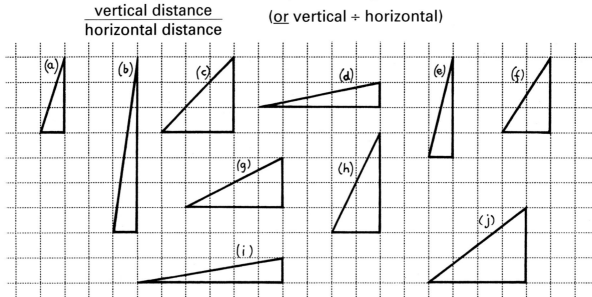

Which of these has (i) the greatest gradient?
(ii) the least gradient?

26 (a)   The drawing shows the approximate cross-section (a slice down the middle) of a hill in North Yorkshire.
Write down the gradient of (i) AB   (ii) BC   (iii) CD   (iv) DE.

(b)   By dividing the total height of the hill by the total length, find the average (mean) gradient of the hill.

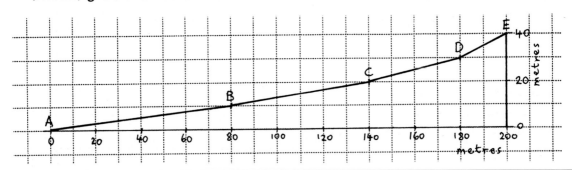

Gradients of graphs
What is the gradient of this graph?

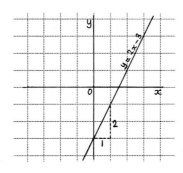

Its gradient is $\frac{2}{1} = 2$

To measure the gradient of a graph, draw a right-angled triangle against it. Then divide the y measurement (up) by the x measurement (along).

Gradient = $\frac{y}{x}$

27 Write down the gradient of each of these graphs.

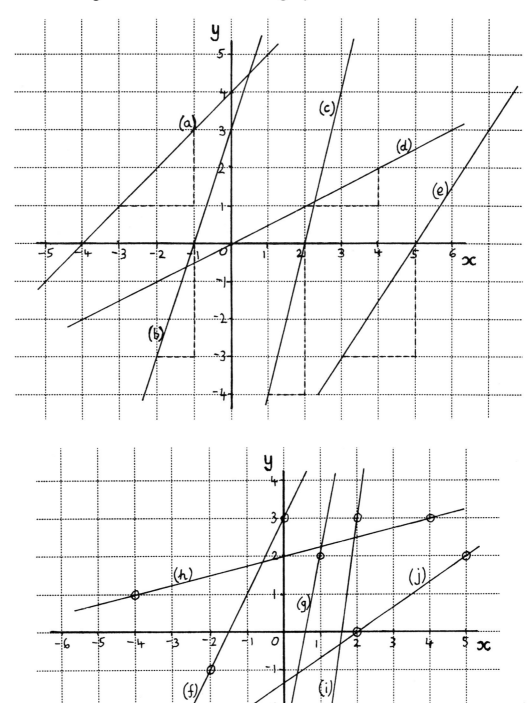

If the equation of a graph begins with y=   , the gradient of the graph can be found by looking at the coefficient of x, e.g.

The gradient of y = 3x − 4 is 3
The gradient of y = $\frac{1}{2}$x + 1 is $\frac{1}{2}$
The gradient of y = x + 4 is 1

28 Without drawing any graphs, write down the gradient of each of these
  (a) $y = 2x - 1$ (g) $y = \frac{1}{3}x$
  (b) $y = 4x$ (h) $y = 5x + \frac{1}{2}$
  (c) $y = 3x + 2$ (i) $y = \frac{x}{2} + 3$
  (d) $y = x - 5$
  (e) $y = \frac{1}{4}x + 3$ (j) $y = \frac{3x}{4}$
  (f) $y = 6x - 7$

29 (i) Draw x and y axes from –7 to +7.
  (ii) Using these axes, draw a straight line graph
    (a) passing through (0,0) and having a gradient of 2
    (b) passing through (1,3) and having a gradient of 1
    (c) passing through (–1,–5) and having a gradient of 3
    (d) passing through (6,6) and having a gradient of $\frac{1}{2}$
    (e) passing through (–6,2) and having a gradient of $\frac{1}{4}$
  (iii) The graphs you have drawn in (ii) should all intersect at one point.
    Write down the coordinates of the point.

Negative gradient

If the direction of a straight line graph is from top-left to bottom-right, its gradient is negative (–), e.g.

GRAPH OF $y = -x$

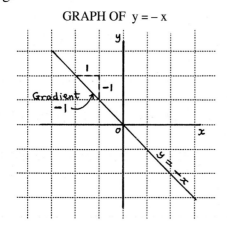

GRAPH OF $y = -2x$

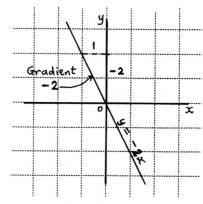

GRAPH OF $y = 2 - 3x$

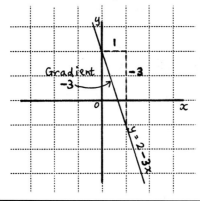

GRAPH OF $y = -\frac{1}{2}x - 1$

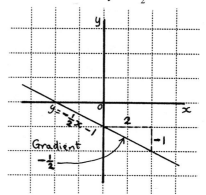

30 Without drawing any graphs, write down the gradient of each of these.
  (a) $y = 4x - 6$ (f) $y = -4x$
  (b) $y = -2x$ (g) $y = 7 - 2x$
  (c) $y = 4 - 3x$ (h) $y = 3x + 10$
  (d) $y = x + 8$ (i) $y = 3 - \frac{1}{2}x$
  (e) $y = 5 - x$ (j) $y = 9 - 5x$

31 Write down the gradient of each of these graphs.

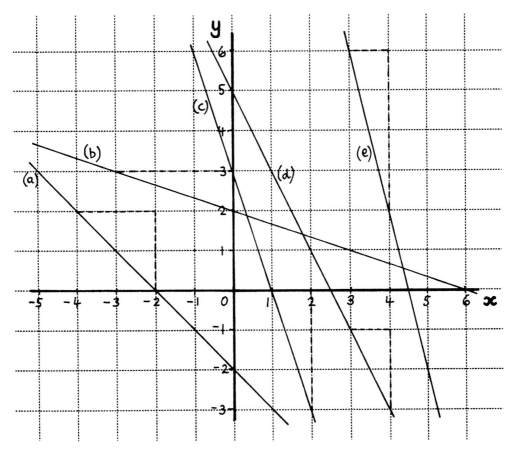

32
(a) Draw x and y axes from −4 to +4.
(b) Plot points A (1,1), B (4,0), C (4,−4), D (−2,−3), E (−4,−4), F (−3,−2), G (−4,4), H (0,4). Join AB, BE, CD, EH, FG, GC, HA.
(c) Write down each of the following and, against each one, write its gradient: EH, GC, AH, FG, EB, AB, DC.
(d) What is the equation of (i) GC, (ii) EH, (iii) EB ?

Another way to draw straight-line graphs

A straight–line graph can be drawn by knowing
   (i)   its gradient (how steep it is)
   (ii) where it crosses the y axis (how far up the ladder it is).

e.g. The graph of y = ⌈ 2 ⌉x ⌈ +1 ⌉

gradient 2   where it crosses the y axis +1

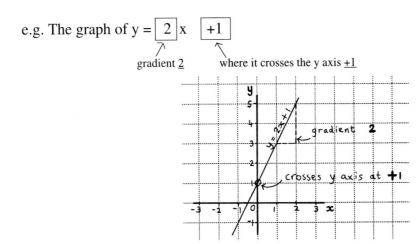

e.g. (2) y = $\boxed{-}$ x $\boxed{+\ 3}$ (or   y = 3 − x)   e.g. (3) y = $\boxed{3}$ x $\boxed{-\ 2}$

gradient −1   crosses y axis at +3   gradient 3   crosses y axis at −2

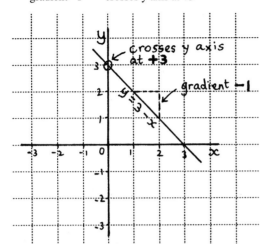 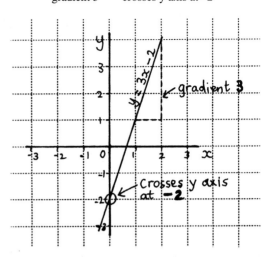

33 By finding (i) the gradient, and (ii) where the graph crosses the y axis, draw the graph of each of these equations. (To avoid confusion, do not put more than two or three graphs on each set of axes.) Label each graph with its equation.

(a)   y = x + 2   (f)   y = $\frac{1}{2}$x + 1
(b)   y = 2x − 1   (g)   y = x + 2$\frac{1}{2}$
(c)   y = 3x   (h)   y = 3x + 5
(d)   y = 4 − x   (i)   y = 3 − 2x
      (or y = −x + 4)   (or y = −2x + 3)
(e)   y = x − 4   (j)   y = 4x − 3

34 For each of these graphs, find   (i) its gradient
                                          (ii) where it crosses the y axis
                                          (iii) its equation

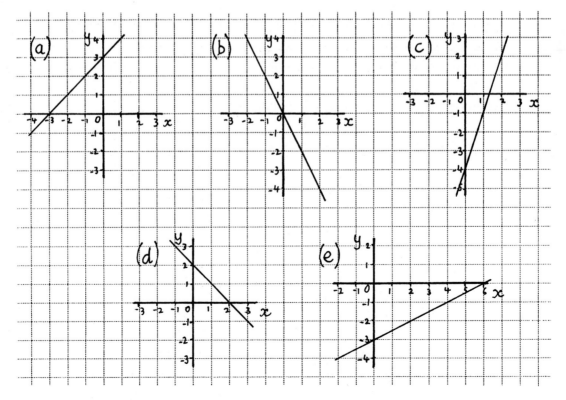

35 Write down the correct equation of each graph.

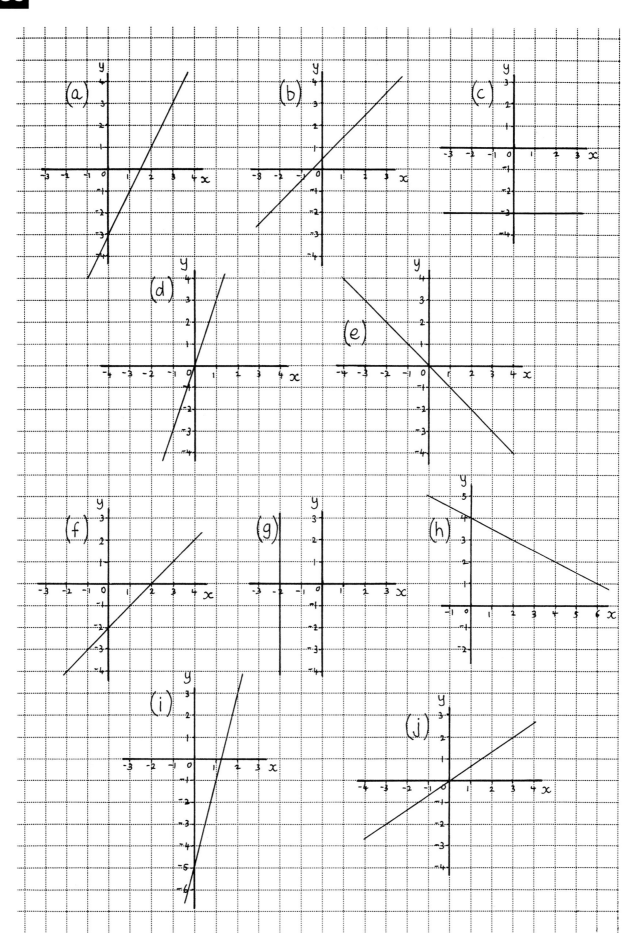

Areas bounded by graphs

Shaded area shows:–

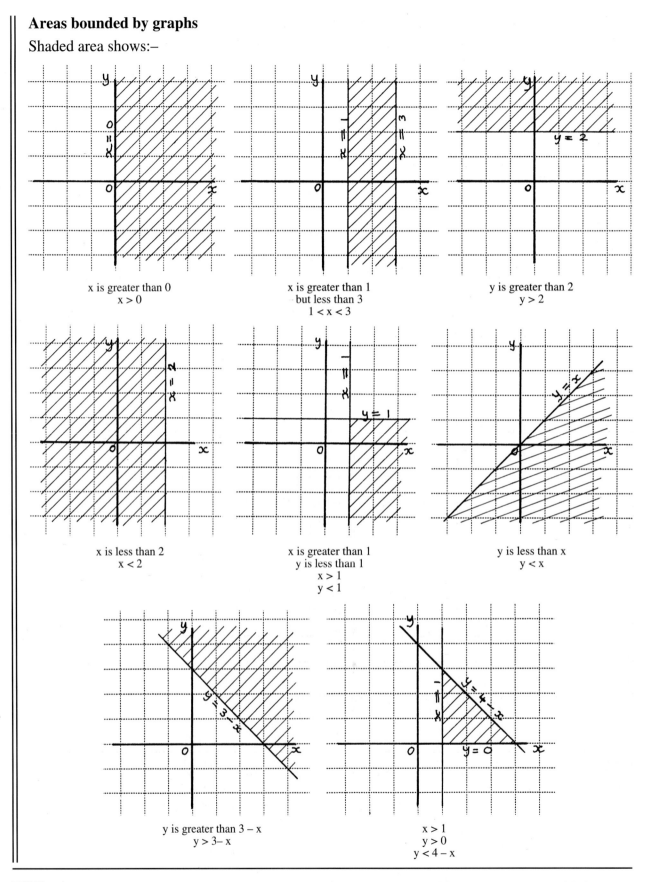

x is greater than 0
x > 0

x is greater than 1
but less than 3
1 < x < 3

y is greater than 2
y > 2

x is less than 2
x < 2

x is greater than 1
y is less than 1
x > 1
y < 1

y is less than x
y < x

y is greater than 3 – x
y > 3– x

x > 1
y > 0
y < 4 – x

36 Both on the same axes, draw graphs of x=2 and x=4. Shade the area which represents 2< x <4

37 Both on the same axes, draw graphs of y=8 and y=x+3. Shade the area in which x>0, y<8, y>x+3.

38 (a) Both on the same axes, draw graphs of y=2x–2 and y=4–x.
    (b) Write down the coordinates of the point where 2x–2 = 4–x.
    (c) Shade the area in which y>2x–2 and y<4–x.

39 (a) Plot points A (–6,0), B (8,8), C (8,7), O (0,0).
    (b) Join AC. Join OB.
    (c) Shade the area which fulfils all the conditions y<$\frac{1}{2}$x + 3, y>x, y>0.

40 (a) Draw graphs of x=–1, x=1, y=4, y=x–2 and y=3x+3 all on the same axes.
    (b) Shade the area in which all the following are true: 1>x>–1, y>x–2,
        y<3x+3, y<4.

41 (a) All on the same axes, draw the graphs of y=2x, y=x–2, y=4–x and y= $\frac{1}{3}$x+3.
    (b) Shade with dots ⬚ the area which satisfies all the conditions y<4–x,
        y<2x, y>x–2.
    (c) Shade with lines ▨ the area which satisfies all the conditions y>x–2,
        y>4–x, y<2x, y<$\frac{1}{3}$x+3.

Solving simultaneous equations by drawing graphs
e.g. Solve the simultaneous equations   y = x + 1
                                            3x – y = 3
Draw the graph of each equation, using one of the methods shown on pages 13, 14 or 19.

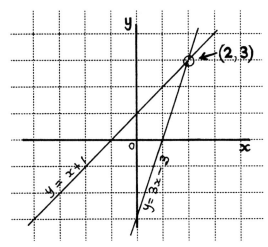

The point of intersection of the two graphs (2,3) gives the solution
$$\begin{cases} x = 2 \\ y = 3 \end{cases}$$

42 Solve these simultaneous equations by drawing graphs.

(a) y = x + 3
    y = 7 – x

(b) y = 2x – 3
    y = x + 1

(c) y = 2x – 9
    x + y = 3

(d) y = 8 – 2x
    y = 3x + 3

(e) y = 2x + 6
    x + y = 0

(f) y = x – 2
    y = 2x – 7

(g) y = x + 10
    y = 2 – x

(h) x – y = 5
    $\frac{1}{2}$x – y = 4

(i) y = 4x + 5
    y = 2x + 1

(j) y = x + 7
    y = 3x + 2

TRANSFORMATIONS

TRANSFORMATIONS (changing one figure into another) include TRANSLATION,
REFLECTION (see page 30), ROTATION (see page 41), ENLARGEMENT (see page 48) and
others.

TRANSLATION

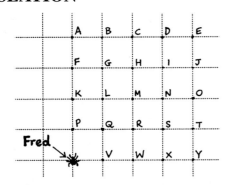

Fred is a spider.
If he moves along 2 squares he will be
on letter W.
If he moves up 3 squares he will be on
letter F.
If he moves along 2 squares and then up
3 squares he will be on letter H.

---

43 Starting from Fred's original position,
  - (a) if he moves along 4 squares and up 2 squares, which letter will he be on?
  - (b) if he moves along 2 squares and up 1 square, which letter will he be on?
  - (c) how many squares along and how many squares up must he move to be on D?
  - (d) how many squares along and how many squares up must he move to be on J?

Fred's journeys can be written in short $\begin{pmatrix} \text{ALONG} \\ \text{UP} \end{pmatrix}$

To move to T he must go along 4 and up 1. This can be written in short $\begin{pmatrix} 4 \\ 1 \end{pmatrix}$.

To move to X he must go along 3 but not up at all. This can be written
in short $\begin{pmatrix} 3 \\ 0 \end{pmatrix}$

---

44 Fred is starting from his original position each time.

  - (a) If he moves $\begin{pmatrix} 1 \\ 3 \end{pmatrix}$ which letter will he be on?

  - (b) Write in short his journey to D.
  - (c) Write in short his journey to S.
  - (d) Write in short his journey to Y.
  - (e) Write in short his journey to B.
  - (f) Write in short his journey to K.
  - (g) What is the longest journey Fred can make?

Each of Fred's new positions is a **TRANSLATION** of his original position.

The short way of writing each journey, e.g. $\begin{pmatrix} 2 \\ 4 \end{pmatrix}$, is a **SHIFT VECTOR**

---

45 Write the shift vector for translating Fred to
(a) M , (b) Q , (c) I , (d) J , (e) A
If Fred STARTED from R, what shift vector would translate him to each of
these?
(f) D , (g) T , (h) H , (i) Y , (j) B

Translation with x and y axes

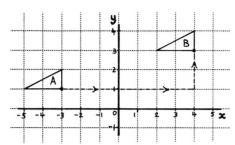

If triangle A is moved along +7 units (squares) and up +2 units $\binom{7}{2}$ the result is triangle B.

Triangle A has been translated with shift vector $\binom{7}{2}$ to give triangle B.

Triangle B is the <u>IMAGE</u> of triangle A, and triangle A <u>MAPS</u> on to triangle B (fits on to it exactly).

Translation can be POSITIVE or NEGATIVE

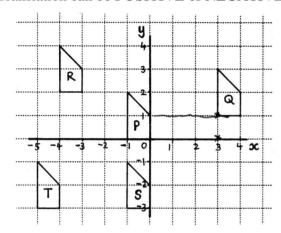

If P is translated $\binom{4}{1}$ it moves
+4 in the x direction and +1 in the y direction to give Q.

If P is translated $\binom{-3}{2}$ it moves
–3 in the x direction and +2 in the y direction to give R.

P translated $\binom{0}{-3}$ gives S.

P translated $\binom{-4}{-3}$ gives T.

When a figure is translated, it stays
> the same way up
> the same way round
> the same size

Note. It is often easier to translate a figure by moving ONE CORNER AT A TIME. Always count VERY CAREFULLY and be sure whether the movement is positive (+) or negative (–)

 In the diagram below, A,B,C,D,E,F,G,U,V,W are all translations of P.
Write each letter and put against it the shift vector of the translation which maps P to the letter.

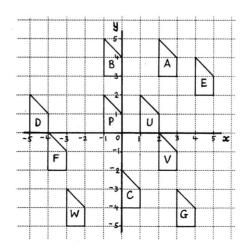

47 (a)   Draw x and y axes with the origin in the centre. Plot points A (–4,–4) and B (–4,–1). Join AB.

(b)   Translate A and B with shift vector $\binom{6}{4}$ to give C and D. Join CD.

Translate AB with shift vector $\binom{2}{2}$ to give EF.

Translate AB $\binom{8}{0}$ to give GH.

Translate AB $\binom{7}{6}$ to give JK.

Translate AB $\binom{0}{5}$ to give LM.

(c)   Write down the shift vector of the translation which maps

(i) EF to JK, (ii) CD to LM, (iii) CD to AB, (iv) LM to GH, (v) JK to CD

(d)   A translation with shift vector $\binom{-3}{1}$ maps GH on to PQ. Draw PQ.

48 (a)   Draw x and y axes. Plot points (3,1), (3,2) and (–1,2). Join the points to form a triangle. Label the triangle A by writing a capital A inside it.

(b)   Translate A with shift vector $\binom{2}{3}$ to give a new triangle B.

(c)   Translate A with shift vector $\binom{1}{-5}$ to give triangle C.

(d)   Translate A with shift vector $\binom{-4}{2}$ to give D.

(e)   Translate A with shift vector $\binom{-3}{-2}$ 3 to give E.

(f)   C maps on to B by translating $\binom{1}{8}$.

Copy and complete:–

E maps on to..... by translating $\binom{5}{5}$

E maps on to D by translating $(\quad)$

D maps on to C by translating ...

B maps on to .... by translating $\binom{-6}{-1}$

.... maps on to E by translating $\binom{-4}{3}$

49 (a)   Draw x and y axes. Plot points A (2,–1), B (1,–2), C (3,–2), D (4,–1), E (3,–1), F (2,0). Join AB, BC, CD, DE, EF, FA to form a figure. Label the figure M by writing a capital M inside it.

(b)   Translate figure M with shift vector $\binom{1}{4}$ to give a new figure R.

(c)   Translate figure R with shift vector $\binom{-7}{-1}$ to give figure S.

(d)   Translate S with shift vector $\binom{3}{-6}$ to give T.

(e)   What translation would map T to M ?

(f)   Translate T $\binom{0}{4}$ to give L.

(g)   What translation would map L to T ?

(h)   What translation would map R to L ?

(i)   How should L be translated to map to M ?

50 (a) Draw x and y axes from 0 to +13. Plot points A (4,1), B (5,2), C (3,2), D (2,1). Join ABCD to form a quadrilateral. Shade or colour the quadrilateral.

(b) Translate ABCD with shift vector $\binom{0}{5}$ so that A maps to E, B maps to F, C maps to G, D maps to H.
Join EFGH to form a quadrilateral. Shade or colour EFGH. Join AE, BF, CG, DH.

(c) Plot J (11,5), K (11,4), L (12,2), M (13,3), N (13,6). Join JKLMN to form a pentagon. Translate JKLMN with shift vector $\binom{-4}{0}$ to give PQRST, so that J maps to P, etc. Shade or colour JKLMN and PQRST.
Join JP, KQ, LR, MS, NT.

(d) Plot U (4,12), V (3,9), W (5,11). Translate the resulting triangle $\binom{6}{0}$ to give XYZ. Join UX, VY, WZ. Colour or shade as before.

(e) Your drawings should look like solid figures. What is this kind of solid called ?

Tessellations

If this rectangle is translated with shift vectors $\binom{2}{0}$, $\binom{0}{1}$ and $\binom{2}{1}$, a regular pattern of 'tiles' can be made

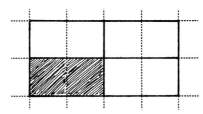

This arrangement of tiles (or plane figures) is a kind of TESSELLATION.
A tessellation is a pattern of tiles (or plane figures) fitting together so that there are no gaps between the tiles.

Example

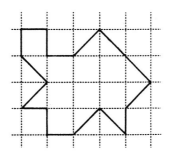

If the tile is translated with shift vectors $\binom{4}{0}$, $\binom{0}{3}$ and $\binom{4}{3}$ a tessellation is formed.

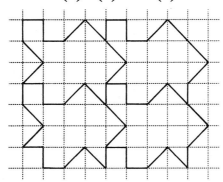

By doing similar translations, the pattern can be extended further.

51 (a)   On squared paper, draw this 'tile' somewhere near the bottom left-hand corner.

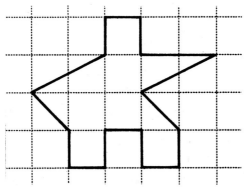

(b)   Translate the tile with shift vector $\begin{pmatrix} 3 \\ 0 \end{pmatrix}$.

Note. An easy way is to trace the tile on to tracing paper (squared if possible), go over the outline exactly with pencil on the back of the tracing paper. Then turn the tracing paper right way up again and press the outline through with a pencil in its new position. To prevent confusion, mark the tracing paper with the word FRONT when you begin the tracing.
Another way is to cut several identical (congruent) tile shapes out of coloured sticky paper and fit the cut-outs together.

(c)   Translate the tile $\begin{pmatrix} 0 \\ 3 \end{pmatrix}$.

(d)   Translate the tile $\begin{pmatrix} 3 \\ 3 \end{pmatrix}$.

(e)   Repeat the translation so that your tessellation covers the whole page.

52 Try making your own tile for a tessellation. Start with a rectangle and change the shape to make it more attractive, but remember ....

(i)   whatever you subtract from the left-hand side you must add to the right-hand side, and vice-versa, e.g.

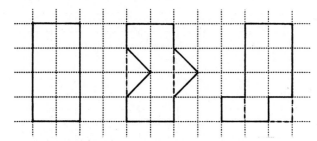

(ii)   whatever you subtract from the top you must add to the bottom, and vice-versa, e.g.

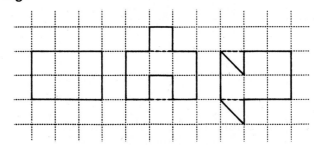

If these rules are followed, your tiles will tessellate (fit together without any gaps). Try designing some tile or wallpaper patterns.

Translations. How to describe them in words.

e.g. Describe the transformation which maps K to L.

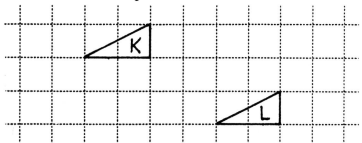

K is translated with shift vector $\begin{pmatrix} 4 \\ -2 \end{pmatrix}$ to map to L, <u>or</u> K maps to L by translation $\begin{pmatrix} 4 \\ -2 \end{pmatrix}$.

53

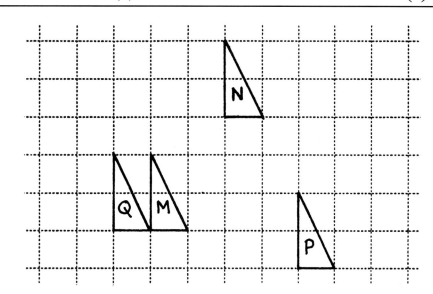

Describe in words the transformation which maps

   (i)   M to N   (iv) N to Q

  (ii)   M to P   (v)   Q to M

 (iii)   P to N

54

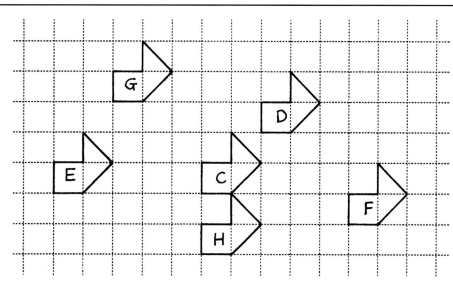

Describe in words the transformation which maps

   (i)   C to D   (iv) C to G

  (ii)   C to E   (v)   C to H

 (iii)   C to F

REFLECTION AND LINE SYMMETRY

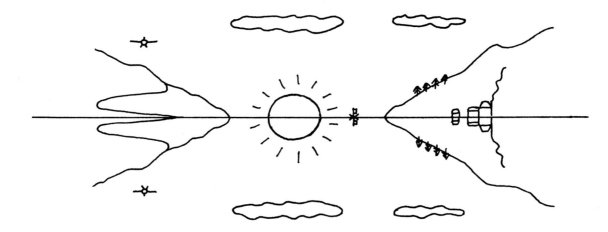

In this drawing, the sun, hills, trees, etc., are reflected in the still water of a lake.

The image of the sun, hills, etc., in the lake is a **REFLECTION.**

The reflection (image) and the original are **SYMMETRICAL** about the horizon. The things below the horizon-line look the same as the things above the horizon-line, but they are all upside down.

In this drawing, the horizon is the **AXIS OF SYMMETRY (or MIRROR LINE).**

---

55 (a)   Fold a piece of paper in half.

(b)   On one half of the folded paper, draw an outline of a shape. This must be a single line, starting at the fold and finishing at the fold.

(c)   Cut along your outline, cutting through both layers of paper (but do not cut along the fold).

(d)   Open out your shape.

<u>Example</u>

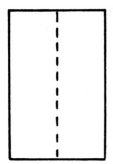   

The complete shape is SYMMETRICAL about the fold.

The fold is the AXIS OF SYMMETRY (<u>or</u> LINE OF SYMMETRY <u>or</u> MIRROR LINE).

The complete shape has LINE SYMMETRY.

One side of the shape is a REFLECTION of the other side.

56 Copy or trace these symmetrical drawings. Then, on your copy, draw an axis of symmetry (mirror line) on each drawing.

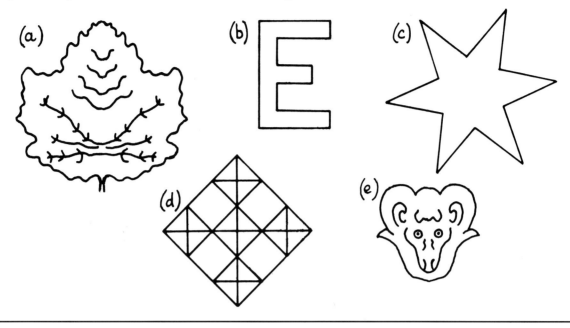

(a) (b) (c) (d) (e)

57 Copy each drawing and complete it so that it is symmetrical about the dotted line.

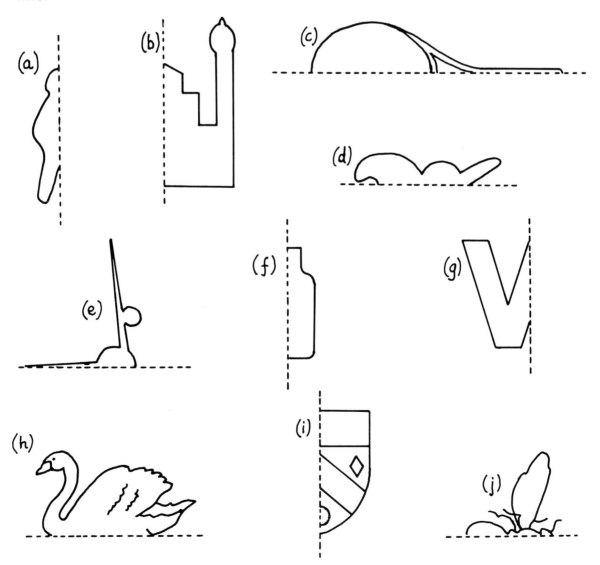

(a) (b) (c) (d) (e) (f) (g) (h) (i) (j)

When a figure is reflected, its image is always
(a)   exactly opposite the original figure. A line joining a point to its reflection is at 90°
       (perpendicular) to the mirror line;
(b)   exactly the same distance from the mirror line as the original figure, but on the other side
       of the mirror line,
e.g.

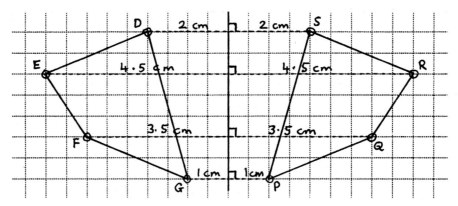

Mathematical mirrors are **double-sided,** e.g. S is the reflection of D, and D is the reflection of S.
When reflecting a figure, it is a good idea to reflect ONE CORNER (or point) AT A TIME, and
then join the corners or points.

58 Copy or trace each of these and draw its reflection. The mirror line in each one
        is marked M.L. Remember that mathematical mirrors are double-sided.

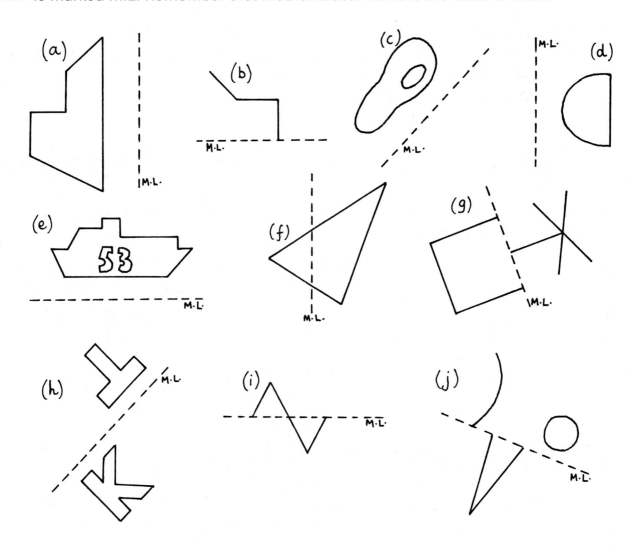

The semaphore alphabet was invented for signalling messages which were spelled out by the sending person and observed by the receiving person. The letters in the drawing are how the receiving person would see them.

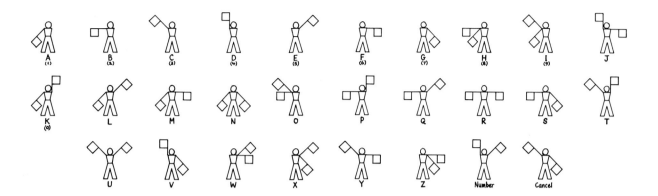

In this alphabet, some letters are reflections (mirror images) of others. Examples.

A is a reflection of G   X is a reflection of I

(a) Find all the other pairs of reflecting semaphore letters. (No need to draw them. Just write the pairs of letters)

(b) What is this message?

Reflection with x and y axes

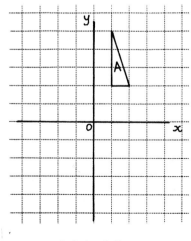

Original figure

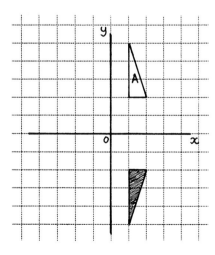

Reflection in x axis
(Reflection in the line y=0)

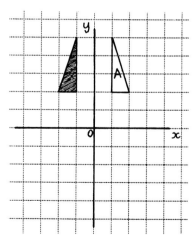

Reflection in y axis
(Reflection in the line x=0)

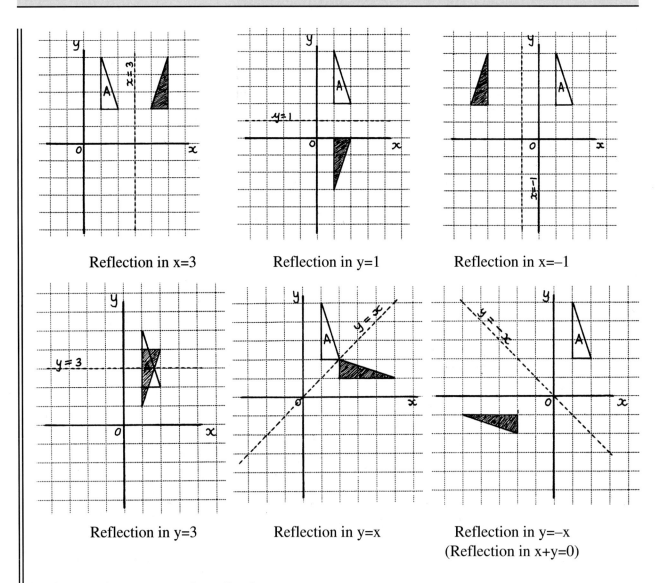

Reflection in x=3   Reflection in y=1   Reflection in x=−1

Reflection in y=3   Reflection in y=x   Reflection in y=−x
                                                                 (Reflection in x+y=0)

Using tracing paper to do reflections

(Squared tracing paper is the best sort)

e.g. Reflect figure B in the line x = 2

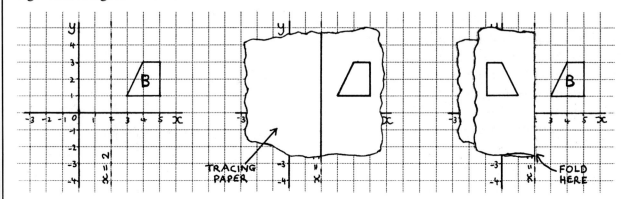

Trace the figure and the mirror line on to the tracing paper.

Keeping the tracing paper <u>in the same position,</u> fold the paper at the mirror line so that your traced figure is reflected.

Press the corners of the reflected figure through with the point of a pencil. Take the tracing paper off and draw the reflected figure accurately.

NOTE. If the figure you want to reflect is on <u>both sides</u> of the mirror line, e.g. question 58 (f) on page 32, you should repeat the method, but fold the tracing paper in the opposite direction (left to right instead of right to left). Another way is to turn the tracing paper completely over (back to front).

Reflections on the mirror line

Any point ON THE MIRROR LINE reflects on to itself, i.e. it stays where it is,

e.g.

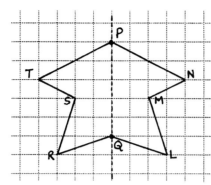

When figure PQRST is reflected in the mirror line

T maps to N

S maps to M

R maps to L

P maps to P

Q maps to Q

The points P and Q, which are ON THE MIRROR LINE, reflect on to themselves.

60

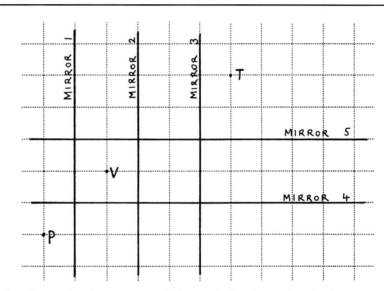

Remember. In a reflection, the image and the original are both the same distance from the mirror. The image is exactly opposite the original.

(a) Copy the diagram on to squared paper.

(b) Reflect P in mirror 5 to give Y (Reflect point P in mirror 5 and call the new point Y).

(c) Reflect Y in mirror 1 to give X.

(d) Reflect T in mirror 3 to give U.

(e) Reflect P in mirror 3 to give Q.

(f) Reflect V in mirror 2 to give W.

(g) Reflect V in mirror 3 to give S.

(h) Reflect Q in mirror 4 to give R.

(i) Join PQRSTUVWXYP (in that order) to form a letter of the alphabet.

---

61 (a) Draw x and y axes from –6 to +6 with the origin in the centre of the page

(b) Plot points A (3,6), B (1,1), C (6,3), D (6,6). Join AB, BC, CD, DA to form a kite.

(c) Reflect A in the x axis to give H, reflect B in the x axis to give J, reflect C in the x axis to give K, reflect D in the x axis to give L.
Join HJKL to form a kite.

(d) Write down the coordinates of H,J,K and L.

(e) Reflect kite ABCD in the y axis to give kite QRST so that A maps to Q, B maps to R, etc.

(f) Write down the coordinates of Q,R,S and T.

62
(a)   Draw x and y axes with the origin (0,0) in the centre of the page.
(b)   Plot points R (3,4), S (2,2) and T (3,2) and join them to form a triangle RST.
(c)   Reflect triangle RST in the x axis to give a new triangle ABC.
      Make sure that A is the reflection of R (R maps to A), B is the reflection of S
      (S maps to B), etc.
(d)   Reflect RST in the y axis to give UVW.
(e)   Draw the graph of x=4. Reflect RST in the graph of x=4 to give GHJ.
(f)   Draw the graph of y=1. Reflect RST in the line y=1 to give CDE.

---

63   The drawing shows triangle M and its images N,P,Q,R,S,T,U,V and W formed
by reflecting M in different mirror-lines, e.g. Q is the reflection of M in the line
y = 2.

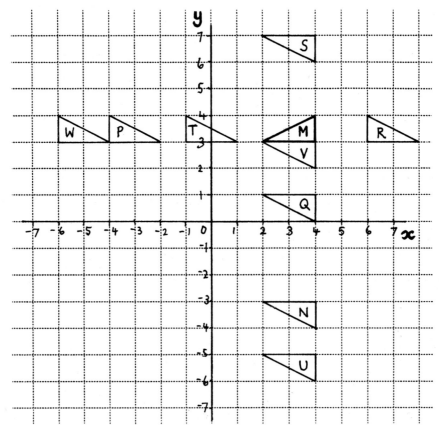

Write down the mirror-line in which M has been reflected to give

(i)	P	(v)	U
(ii)	R	(vi)	W
(iii)	N	(vii)	V
(iv)	S	(viii)	T

64
(a)   Plot points M (2,7), N (1,7), P (2,4), Q (5,3), R (5,5). Join MNPQR to make a
      pentagon.
(b)   Reflect MNPQR in the line x = −1 to give STUVW.
(c)   Write down the coordinates of V.
(d)   Reflect MNPQR in the line y = 1$\frac{1}{2}$ to give ABCDE.
(e)   Write down the coordinates of E.
(f)   Reflect MNPQR in the line x = 2 to form MLPJK.
(g)   Join AW, ES, AK, EM. What special kind of quadrilateral are AESW and
      AEMK ?

65
  (a) Draw x and y axes and mark them each from –6 to +6.

  (b) Plot points (3,4), (0,4) and (1,2). Join the points to make a triangle. Label the triangle P.

  (c) Reflect triangle P in the y axis to give Q.

  (d) Reflect Q in the line y=4 to give R.

  (e) Reflect P in the x axis to give S.

  (f) Reflect S in the line x=2 to give T.

  (g) Reflect T in the line x=–1 to give U.

66

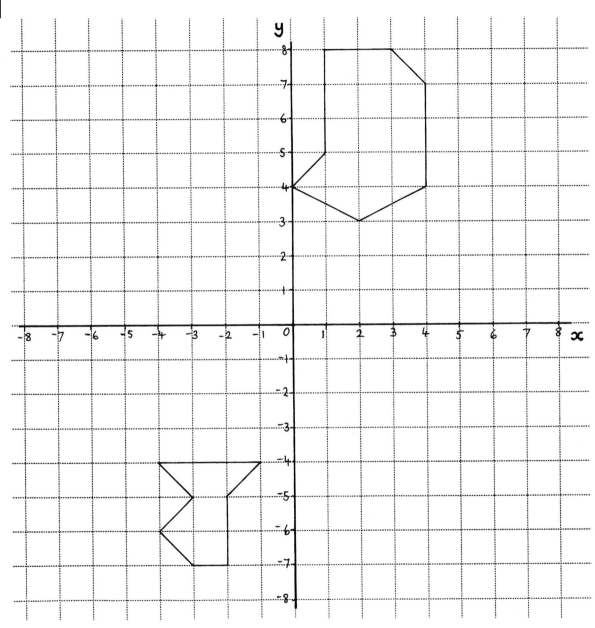

  (a) Copy the drawing on to squared paper.

  (b) Draw the graph of y = x.

  (c) Reflect both figures in the line y = x.

  (d) Draw the graph of y = –x.

  (e) Reflect in the line y = –x everything you have already drawn.

67

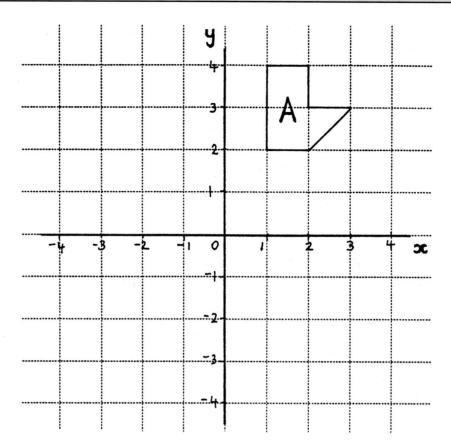

(a) Copy the drawing on to squared paper.
(b) Reflect figure A in the x axis to give B.
(c) Reflect A in the y axis to give C.
(d) Reflect C in the x axis to give D.
(e) Draw the graph of y=x. Reflect A in y=x to give E.
(f) Reflect E in the y axis to give F.
(g) Reflect E and F in the x axis to give a figure which is symmetrical about both axes (i.e. the bottom reflects the top and the right reflects the left).

68 (a) Plot points O (0,0), A (4,0), B (3,1), C (3,3), D (1,3), E (0,4).
(b) Join ABCDEO to make a six-sided figure.
(c) Draw the graph of y = 6 − x
(d) Reflect ABCDEO in the graph of y = 6 − x to give FGCHJK.
(e) Reflect ABCDEO and FGCHJK in the x axis and the y axis.
(f) Complete to make the drawing symmetrical about the x axis and symmetrical about the y axis.

69 (a) Draw x and y axes from −6 to +6. Plot (5,1), (5,2), (4,2) and (3,1). Join these points (in this order) to form a trapezium E.
(b) Reflect trapezium E in the x axis. Draw the image and mark with the letter F.
(c) Reflect E in the y axis to give image G.
(d) Reflect E in the line x=2 to give H.
(e) Reflect E in the line y=3 to give J.
(f) Reflect E in the line y=x to give K.
(g) When G is translated with shift vector $\binom{4}{0}$, it maps to H.

What translation maps F to J ?

70 A kaleidoscope is a tube containing three mirrors fixed in the shape of an equilateral triangle. When objects, such as small pieces of coloured glass or plastic, are viewed through the tube, the reflections are seen also, forming a symmetrical pattern,
e.g.

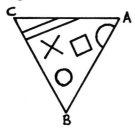

ORIGINAL PATTERN

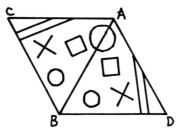

Original pattern
reflected in AB

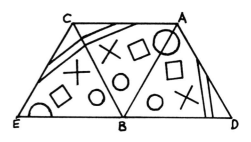

Original pattern
reflected in AB and BC

(a) Trace triangle ABC. Then, using the tracing (either back or front upwards, whichever gives the correct reflection), reflect ABC in the line AB to give ABD.

(b) Continue the pattern until you have made a large hexagon containing 24 triangles.

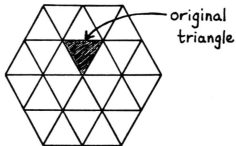

original triangle

(c) Make your own pattern in an equilateral triangle. Then repeat (a) and (b).

71

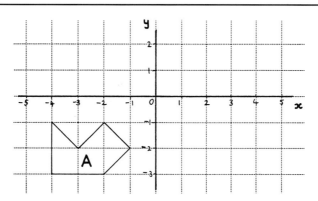

(i) Draw x and y axes from –7 to +7. Copy shape A in the position shown.

(ii) Reflect A in the line x=1 to give B.

(iii) Translate A with shift vector $\begin{pmatrix} 6 \\ 5 \end{pmatrix}$ to give C.

(iv) Reflect A in the line y=0 to give D.

(v) Translate D $\begin{pmatrix} 6 \\ -1 \end{pmatrix}$ to give E.

(vi) Describe the transformation which maps E to C.

(vii) Reflect C in the line x = –1 to give F.

(viii) Describe the transformation which maps F to B.

Translations and reflections. How to describe them in words.

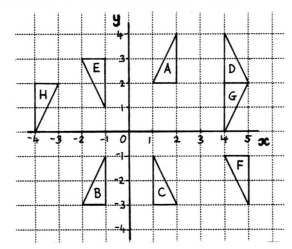

e.g.   Describe the translation or reflection which maps A to B.
Is this a translation or a reflection?
A translation, because A and B are both the same way up and the same way round.

Answer. A maps to B by translation with shift vector $\begin{pmatrix} -3 \\ -5 \end{pmatrix}$.

e.g. (2) Describe the transformation which maps B to E.
Is this a translation or a reflection?
A reflection, because B and E are opposite one another but different ways round.
Answer. B maps to E by reflection in the x axis (or reflection in the line y = 0).

---

72 Look at the drawing above, and describe in words the transformation (translation or reflection) which maps

(i)	B to A	(iv)	E to F
(ii)	A to D	(v)	H to G
(iii)	C to B	(vi)	G to D

73

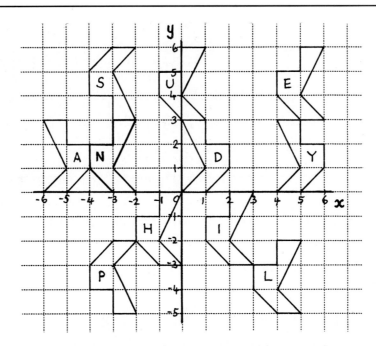

Figures A,D,E,H,I,L,P,S,U and Y are all transformations of figure N by either translation or reflection. Write down each letter and describe in words the transformation which maps N to the letter.

ROTATION AND ROTATIONAL SYMMETRY

ROTATION means 'turning'. When a figure is ROTATED, it turns <u>about</u> (or around) a fixed point called the <u>centre of rotation</u>, e.g.

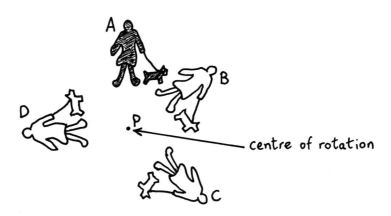

B,C and D are images of A, when A is rotated about the point P.
P is the centre of rotation.

<u>To do rotation successfully</u>, you need to know
1) how far (through what angle should the figure be rotated?),

2) which way (clockwise ⌢↘ or anticlockwise ↙⌢ , except for rotations through 180° which are the same either way),

3) about which point (where is the centre of rotation?).

The simplest kinds of rotation are
(a) through 180° (half way round, <u>or</u> a half turn)
(b) through 90° clockwise (quarter way round, <u>or</u> a quarter turn)
(c) through 90° anticlockwise (quarter way round, <u>or</u> a quarter turn)

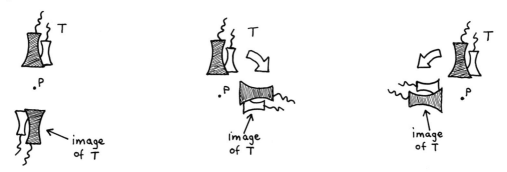

| T rotated through 180° about P | T rotated through 90° clockwise about P | T rotated through 90° anticlockwise about P |

If all three of these rotations are combined in one drawing, the complete figure has ROTATIONAL SYMMETRY of ORDER 4.

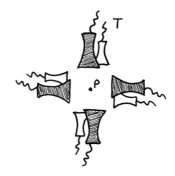

Rotational symmetry

A figure has ROTATIONAL SYMMETRY if it maps (or fits) exactly on to itself when it is turned to face a different way, e.g.

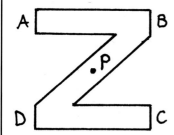

This figure can be rotated about point P so that A maps to C, B maps to D, C maps to A, D maps to B, etc.

Trace the figure. Then, keeping the tracing paper in place, hold it down with a pencil point at P. Turn the tracing paper through 180° to show that the figure fits on to itself.

This figure has ROTATIONAL SYMMETRY of ORDER 2, because the figure fits exactly in 2 different ways.

If it fits 3 different ways, it has ROTATIONAL SYMMETRY of ORDER 3, etc.

A figure that <u>does not rotate on to itself</u> (except by turning it back to its original position) has NO ROTATIONAL SYMMETRY, e.g.

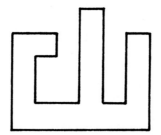

---

74 Write down whether each of these figures has rotational symmetry. If it has, write down its ORDER of rotational symmetry; if it has not, write 'NO ROTATIONAL SYMMETRY'.

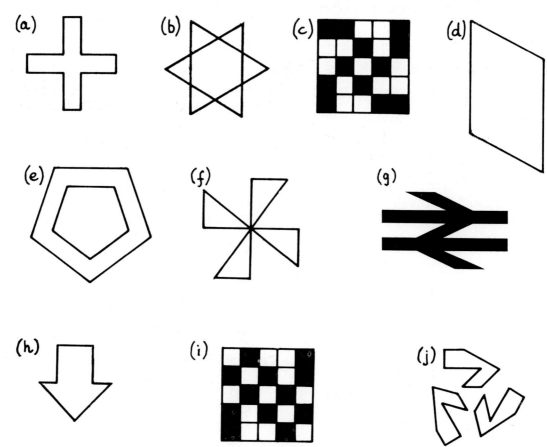

Rotation with x and y axes

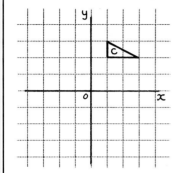

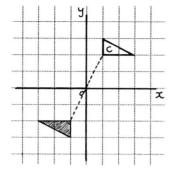

Rotation 180°
about the origin (0,0)

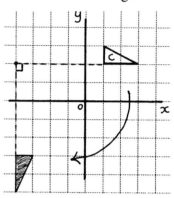

Rotation 90° clockwise
about the origin

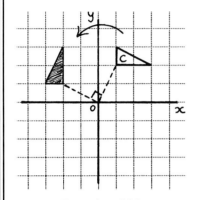

Rotation 90°
anti-clockwise
about the origin

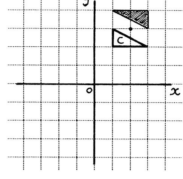

Rotation 180°
about the point (2,3)

Rotation 90° clockwise
about the point (–4,2)

NOTE. Clockwise rotation is sometimes called NEGATIVE rotation, e.g.
A rotation of 90° clockwise is a rotation of –90°.
Anticlockwise rotation is sometimes called POSITIVE rotation, e.g.
A rotation of 90° anticlockwise is a rotation of +90°

Rotation of a point at the centre of rotation

A point which is exactly on the centre of rotation rotates on to itself, i.e. it stays where it is, e.g.

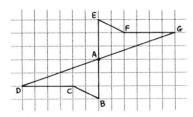

When figure ABCD rotates 180° about
the point A
  B rotates to E
  C rotates to F
  D rotates to G
  A rotates to A

Reflection in a point

Rotation through 180° has the same effect as REFLECTING IN A POINT,
e.g.

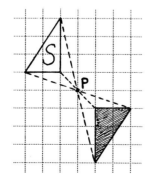

Triangle S has been rotated 180° about point P.

Triangle S has also been REFLECTED in point P.

(Triangle S has also been ENLARGED with scale
factor –1 and centre of enlargement P. See page 49)

Using tracing paper to do rotations
(Squared tracing paper is the best sort)

e.g. Rotate figure R through 90° anticlockwise about the point (1,1)

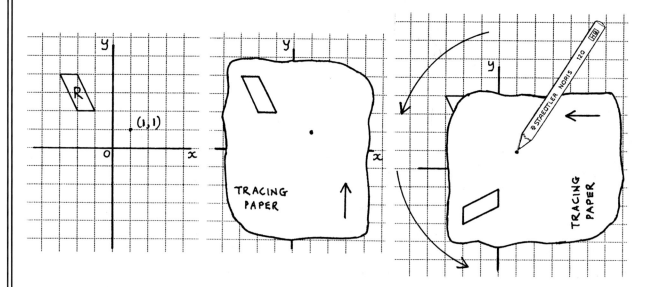

Trace <u>the figure</u> and <u>the centre of rotation</u> on to the tracing paper.

Also, on the tracing paper, draw an arrow pointing straight upwards (pretend it is North).

Press a pencil point firmly on to the tracing of the centre of rotation. Turn the tracing paper the correct amount. Press the corners of the rotated figure through with the point of a pencil. Then take the tracing paper off and draw the rotated figure accurately.

The arrow ↑ on your tracing paper should face

↓ (South) for a rotation of 180°

→ (East) for a rotation of 90° clockwise

← (West) for a rotation of 90° anticlockwise

---

75 (a)   Plot M (3,2).
Rotate M (i) through 180° with centre of rotation O (0,0) to give M_1,
(ii) through 90° clockwise about O to give M_2
(iii) through 90° anticlockwise about O to give M_3

(b)   Plot N (2,7). Rotate N in the same ways as part (a) to give N_1, N_2, N_3

(c)   Plot P (6,7). Rotate P in the same ways as part (a) to give P_1, P_2, P_3

(d)   Plot Q (6,4). Rotate Q in the same ways as part (a) to give Q_1, Q_2, Q_3

(e)   Join OM, MN, NP, PQ.

(f)   Rotate OM, MN, NP, PQ in the same ways as part (a).

---

76 (a)   Copy this figure carefully on to squared paper. (The squares can be any size.)

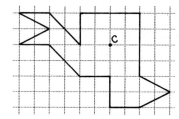

(b)   Rotate the figure about C through 180°.

(c)   Rotate the figure about C through 90° clockwise.

(d)   Rotate the figure about C through 90° anticlockwise.

77 (a) Plot points A (1,2), B (3,3), C (2,5), D (1,5). Join ABCD to form a quadrilateral.

(b) Rotate ABCD 180° about the origin (0,0) to give quadrilateral EFGH. Point A should map to E, etc.

(c) Write down the coordinates of F.

(d) Rotate ABCD 90° clockwise about the origin to give JKLM.

(e) Write down the coordinates of J.

(f) Rotate ABCD 90° anticlockwise about the origin to give PQRS.

(g) Join AJEP. Join DMHS. What special kind of quadrilateral are AJEP and DMHS?

78 (a) Plot points (1,2), (1,3) and (3,3). Join the points to make a triangle. Label the triangle D (Write letter D inside the triangle.).

(b) Rotate triangle D in the following ways:–

(i) 180° about the point (3,1) to give triangle E.

(ii) 180° about (–1,4) to give F.

(iii) 90° clockwise about (1,1) to give G.

(iv) 90° clockwise about (–3,3) to give H.

(v) 90° anticlockwise about (1,5) to give J.

(vi) 90° anticlockwise about (2,–2) to give K.

(vii) 180° about (2,3) to give L.

(viii) 90° anticlockwise about (0,–1) to give M.

79 (a) Plot points Q (–5,1), R (5,7), S (–1, –5). Join to form a triangle.

(b) Rotate QRS 180° about (1,1) to give MNP. Make sure the new triangle is labelled correctly: Q maps to M, etc.

(c) Rotate QRS 90° clockwise about (–3,0) to give BCD.

(d) Rotate MNP 90° anticlockwise about (1,2) to give GHJ.

(e) Join CJ, and write down the coordinates of the mid-point of CJ.

80

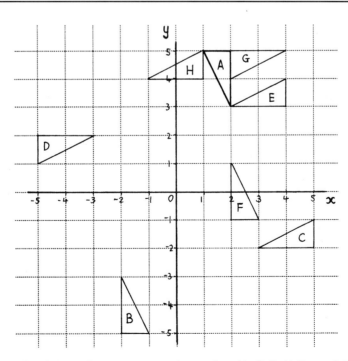

In this drawing, triangle A has been rotated to give B,C,D,E,F and G.
Describe fully the rotation which maps A to each of the others, e.g.

A to H : 90° clockwise, centre of rotation (1,5).

81 (a) Plot points (3,–1), (1,–4), (3,–4), (3,–3) and (4,–2). Join these points in the same order, also joining the last point to the first, to make a concave pentagon. Label the pentagon with the letter R.

(b) Rotate pentagon R as follows
(i) 90° anticlockwise about (2,–6) to give N.
(ii) 90° clockwise about (6,2) to give K.
(iii) 180° about (0,–2) to give F.
(iv) 90° clockwise about (1,5) to give Z.
(v) 180° about (2,0) to give Q.
(vi) 90° anticlockwise about (–4,0) to give B.

---

82 (a) Using graph paper with <u>2mm squares</u>, draw x and y axes with the origin (0,0) in the middle of the page, and with 1 square to represent 1 unit. Plot points A (8,34), B (10,40), C (19,39), D (20,34), E (25,31), F (29,28), G (37,28). Join AB, BC, CD, DE, EF, FG with straight dotted lines.

(b) ABCDEFG is a rough outline of one of the constellations of stars in the night sky (North of the Equator only). What is the name of this constellation?

(c) At different times of the year and different times of the night, the constellation changes its position in the sky.
Rotate ABCDEFG about O (0,0) through 180°, 90° clockwise and 90° anticlockwise to show three other possible positions.

(d) The origin O (0,0) in your drawing also represents a star. Travellers once found this star, which showed them approximately where North was, by producing BA roughly to O so that AO was about 5x BA. What is the name of the star represented by (0,0) which always points roughly North?

---

83 (a) Plot points (–6,3), (–5,2), (–3,2), (–4,3), (–3,4), (–5,4). Join these in the same order to form a hexagon H.

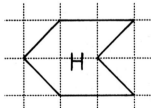

(b) Rotate H through 90° anticlockwise about (3,4) to give J.
(c) Rotate H through 180° about (–1,2) to give K.
(d) Rotate K through 90° clockwise about (5,6) to give L.
(e) Rotate J through 180° about (–1,1) to give M.
(f) Rotate K through 90° anticlockwise about (0,–4) to give N.
(g) Plot (0,3), (3,3), (3,5), (0,5). Join to make a rectangle.
(h) Rotate the rectangle <u>either</u> 90° clockwise with centre of rotation (–1,–1) <u>or</u> 90° anticlockwise with centre of rotation (6½, 1½).
The rectangle should 'capture' J (just fit round it).
(i) By experimenting, and with the help of tracing paper, find which centre of rotation is needed for the rectangle to rotate and 'capture' these
(i) H
(ii) K
(iii) L (two possible answers)
(iv) M (two possible answers)
(v) N (two possible answers)

84 (a) Plot points (3,1), (5,1), (6,4), (4,4). Join to form a parallelogram. Label the parallelogram A.

    (b) Rotate parallelogram A 180° about (2,1) to give B.

(c) Rotate B 90° clockwise about (–1,3) to give C.

(d) Rotate C 90° anticlockwise about (–2,2) to give D.

(e) Rotate D 180° about (–3,–2) to give E.

(f) REFLECT E in the y axis to give F.

(g) Rotate A 180° about (–$\frac{1}{2}$,2) to give G..

(h) REFLECT F in the line y=–2 to give H.

(i) TRANSLATE E with shift vector $\begin{pmatrix} 5 \\ 3 \end{pmatrix}$ to give J.

85

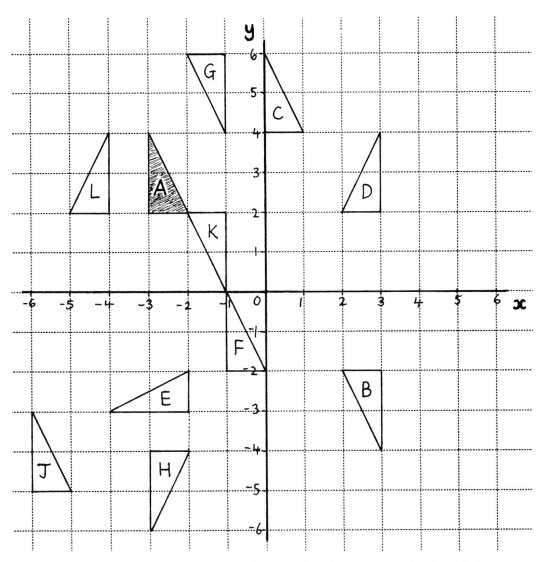

Describe fully the transformation (translation, reflection or rotation) which maps triangle A on to each of B, C, D, E, F, G, H, J, K and L.

In each case, say whether it is a translation, reflection or rotation.

If a translation, state the <u>shift vector</u>;

if a reflection, say which is the <u>mirror-line</u>;

if a rotation, state <u>direction</u>, <u>amount</u> and <u>centre of rotation.</u>

ENLARGEMENT

An enlargement of a photograph is a larger copy of the photograph,
e.g.

Original

Enlargement

Enlargement

In mathematics, an enlargement can be **larger than, smaller than** or **the same size as** the original. The image (the enlargement of the original) is similar to the original, i.e. exactly the same shape.

An enlargement is measured from a point called the **CENTRE OF ENLARGEMENT.**

The **size of the image** and the **distance of the image from the original** depend on the **SCALE FACTOR** of the enlargement.

e.g. To construct an enlargement of triangle ABC with centre of enlargement P.

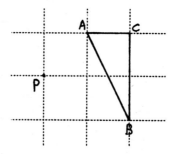

Join PA, PB, PC.
For an enlargement with <u>scale factor 2</u>,
produce PA to F so that distance PF is   2 x distance PA,
produce PB to G so that distance PG is   2 x distance PB,
produce PC to H so that distance PH is   2 x distance PC.
Then join FGH to make a triangle.

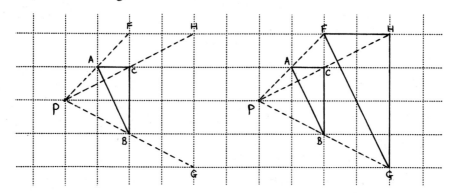

FGH is the image of ABC under an enlargement with centre of enlargement P and scale factor 2.

For an enlargement with <u>scale factor 3,</u>
produce PA to R so that PR = 3 x PA, etc.

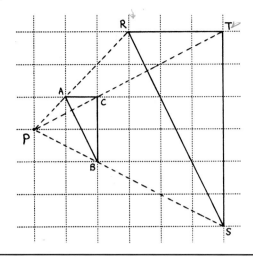

If the scale factor is a fraction of a unit (a number greater than 0 but less than 1), the image is SMALLER than the original, e.g. Quadrilateral Q can be enlarged with centre of enlargement C and scale factor $\frac{1}{2}$ to give quadrilateral R.

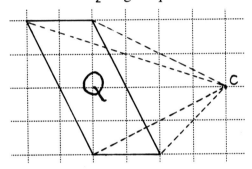
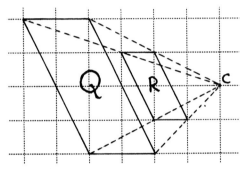

If the scale factor is a **NEGATIVE** number, the image is on the <u>opposite side</u> of the centre of enlargement, e.g.

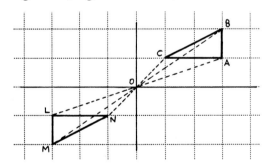

An enlargement of triangle ABC with centre of enlargement 0 and <u>scale factor –1</u> gives triangle LMN.

An enlargement of the same triangle ABC with centre of enlargement 0 and <u>scale factor –2</u> gives triangle TUV. Distance OT is 2 x distance OA, etc.

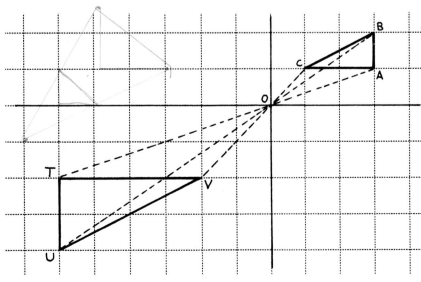

Area of enlarged figure

The area of the image equals the area of the original multiplied by the SQUARE OF THE SCALE FACTOR, e.g.

For an enlargement with scale factor 2, the area of the image is 2^2 or $2 \times 2 = 4$ times the area of the original.

e.g. (2) Rectangle K undergoes an enlargement with scale factor 3 to give rectangle M.

Area of rectangle M = 3 x 3 x area of rectangle K

Area of K is 2 square units, so area of M = 3 x 3 x 2 = 18 square units.

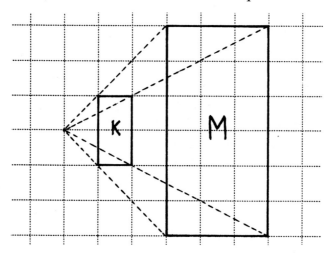

Finding the centre of enlargement

Join two or more corresponding (similar) corners of figures, and produce the lines until they intersect, e.g.

Find the centre of enlargement in this construction.

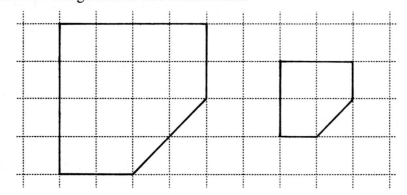

By joining corresponding corners, the centre of enlargement is found.

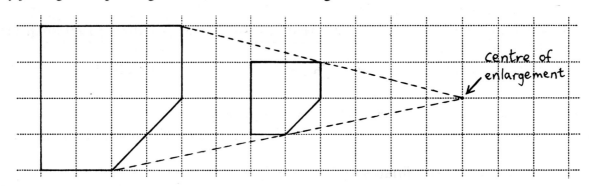

86 Draw a triangle with vertices (corners) B (1,3), C (4,2), D (2,2). With O (0,0) as the centre of enlargement, and scale factor 2, construct an enlargement of the triangle and label it PQR. B should map to P, etc.

87 (a) Plot points E (–2,6), F (–3,5), G (–2,2), H (–1,5). Join EFGHE to form a kite.
(b) With centre of enlargement C (–7,6) and scale factor 2, draw an enlargement KLMN with E mapping to K, F mapping to L, etc.
(c) FE and LK should be parallel. Write down three other sets of parallel lines.

88 (a) Plot points K (1,3), L (5,3), M (4,5). Join KLM to make a triangle.
(b) With centre of enlargement (5,7) and scale factor 3, enlarge triangle KLM to give triangle STU.
(c) Write down the coordinates of point S.
(d) What is the area (in square units) of triangle KLM ?
(e) Work out, without measuring, the area of triangle STU. Check your answer by measuring.

89 (a) Draw a quadrilateral with vertices (–2,7), (–4,7), (–3,4) and (–2,6).
(b) With centre of enlargement (–3,8) and scale factor 4, construct an enlargement of the quadrilateral.
(c) The area of your original quadrilateral should be $3\frac{1}{2}$ square units. Calculate the area of the enlarged quadrilateral and check your answer by measuring.

90 Draw triangle CDE with C (3,5), D (4,2), E (2,3).
With scale factor –2 and centre of enlargement (2,1), enlarge triangle CDE to give image triangle FGH, with C mapping to F, D mapping to G, E mapping to H.

91 (a) Draw a triangle with vertices (3,–6), (3,–2) and (1,–2). Label the triangle H.
(b) Construct an enlargement of H with centre of enlargement (1,–5) and scale factor 2. Label the image J.
(c) Construct an enlargement of H with centre of enlargement (0,0) and scale factor –1. Label the image K.
(d) Construct an enlargement of <u>K</u> with centre of enlargement (–7,–6) and scale factor $\frac{1}{2}$. Label the image L.

92 (a) Plot points A (–4,5), B (1,0), C (–4,–5), D (–4,–10), E (–9,–5). Join AB, BC, CD, DE, EA to form a pentagon.
(b) Plot points J (8,–1), M (8,2). Join AJ, DM and mark the intersection of AJ and DM with letter P.
(c) P is the centre of an enlargement mapping ABCDE to JKLMN. Complete JKLMN and join to form a pentagon.
(d) What is the scale factor of the enlargement which maps ABCDE to JKLMN ?

93 (a) Draw triangle JKL with J (5,2), K (2,3), L (6,4).
(b) Enlarge triangle JKL with centre of enlargement (5,3) and scale factor 3 to give RST.
(c) Write down the coordinates of R, S and T.

94

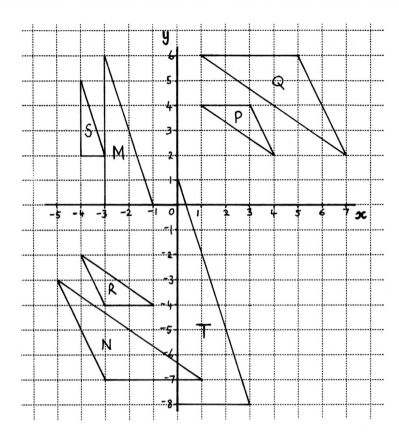

Copy this diagram on to squared paper (1cm squares are probably best), making sure that the coordinates of the triangle corners are correct, e.g. P must be (4,2), (3,4) and (1,4), etc.

Find (i) the coordinates of the centre of enlargement, (ii) the scale factor, for the enlargement which maps
   (a) P to Q,   (b) S to T,   (c) P to R,   (d) S to M,   (e) R to N.

95 (a) Plot points A (0,3), B (2,3), C (2,5), D (1,6), E (0,5).
     Join AB, BC, CD, DE, EA to form a pentagon.
     Plot points F (4,3), G (5,3), H (5,6), J ($4\frac{1}{2}$,6).
     Join FG, GH, HJ (but not JF) to form a three-sided open figure.

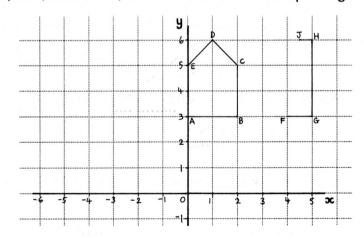

  (b) Construct an enlargement of pentagon ABCDE and figure FGH with centre of enlargement (4,4) and scale factor 2.
  (c) On the same drawing, repeat question (b) with the same centre of enlargement and scale factor 3.

(d) Imagine that your finished drawing is an artist's picture. An artist would call the centre of enlargement the VANISHING POINT. Pretend that you are an artist and you want to draw the picture from a higher viewpoint. On a new page (or new sheet of paper), repeat (a), (b) and (c) but with centre of enlargement (vanishing point) (3,7).

(e) Try the same drawing with other centres of enlargement, e.g. (7,4), and see what effects they produce.

96 The diagram (not to scale) shows a pinhole camera taking a photograph of a vertical pole AB. (A pinhole camera is a box which is light-tight except for a tiny pinhole in the front, and which has photographic film or paper placed inside at the back.) The pinhole is the centre of enlargement.

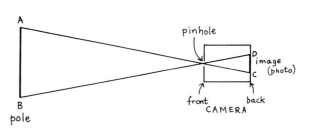

The enlargement of the pole (the image on the photograph) is CD. The camera is 10cm from front to back. The distance from the pole to the front of the camera is 250cm.

(a) What is the enlargement factor? (Remember CD is an enlargement of AB).

(b) The pole is 150cm high. How high is the image of the pole on the photograph?

(c) Which way up is the image ?

(d) How much further away must the pole be moved to make an image 5cm high on the photograph?

97 This is a diagram, seen from the side or from above, of a lamp shining through a rectangular slide and forming a rectangular image (a PROJECTION) on a screen. The image on the screen is an enlargement of the picture on the slide. The scale factor of the enlargement is 7 and the centre of enlargement is the lamp.

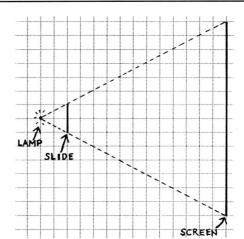

Look at the diagram and try these questions.

(a) If the picture on the slide is 5cm high, how high is the picture on the screen?

(b) If the picture on the slide is 6cm wide, how wide is the picture on the screen?

(c) What is the area of the picture on the slide?

(d) What is the area of the picture on the screen?

(e) If the lamp and slide are kept in the same place as in the diagram, but the distance between the slide and screen is halved
   (i)   what is the scale factor of the enlargement?
   (ii) what is the area of the picture on the screen?

(f) If the slide and screen are kept in the same place as in the diagram, but the distance between the lamp and the slide is multiplied by 3
   (i)   what is the scale factor of the enlargement?
   (ii) what is the area of the picture on the screen?

NOTE. In a real slide projector, lenses have to be added as shown to give a sharp image. By following the rays of light, you can see why a slide has to be put in a projector upside-down to produce a right-way-up image on the screen.

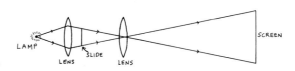

QUADRATIC AND OTHER GRAPHS (Curved Graphs)

To draw graphs in this part of the book, use GRAPH PAPER with 2mm squares.

Drawing a graph from a table of values

e.g. Draw the graph of $y = 2x - 3$, choosing values of x from −1 to +4.

x	−1	0	1	②	3	4
2x	−2	0	2	④	6	8
−3	−3	−3	−3	⊖3	−3	−3
y	−5	−3	−1	①	3	5

e.g.

when x = 2

2x = 4

−3 = −3

y = 4 − 3 = 1

e.g. When x=1,y=−1   When x=4,y=5
giving point (1,−1)   giving (4,5)

Plot the points from the table to give the graph of $y = 2x - 3$

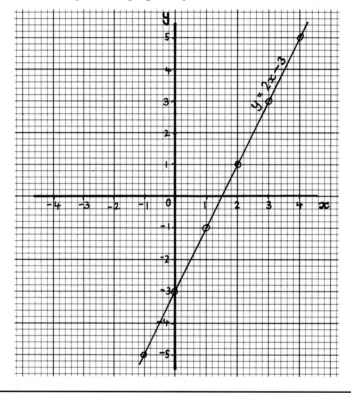

---

98 Draw a table of values for each of these graphs. Choose values of x from −4 to +4.

e.g. $y = 3x + 2$

x	−4	−3	−2	−1	0	1	2	3	4
3x	−12	−9	−6	−3	0	3	6	9	12
+2	+2	+2	+2	+2	+2	+2	+2	+2	+2
y	−10	−7	−4	−1	2	5	8	11	14

(a) $y = 4x + 7$ (d) $y = 6 - \frac{1}{2}x$

(b) $y = 8 - 3x$ (e) $y = x^2 + 4$

(c) $y = 2x - 5$

Quadratic Graphs (Graphs of equations containing x^2)

The graph of an equation containing x^2 (a quadratic graph) is a **curved line** (not a straight line).

Example. Make a table of values for the graph of $y = x^2$, with values of x from –3 to +3. From the table, plot points and draw the graph of $y = x^2$.

x	–3	–2	–1	0	1	2	3
y	9	4	1	0	1	4	9

TABLE OF VALUES

When x = –3, $y = x^2$ which equals x $\times$ x = –3 $\times$ –3 = 9. So when x = –3, y = 9, giving the point (–3,9).

When x = 2, $y = x^2$ = 2 $\times$ 2 = 4. So when x=2, y=4 giving the point (2,4), etc.

REMEMBER. The square of <u>any number</u> is POSITIVE (+).

Plot the points from your table of values. Then join the points with a smooth curve. The curve is a PARABOLA (pronounced pa–<u>rab</u>–ola).

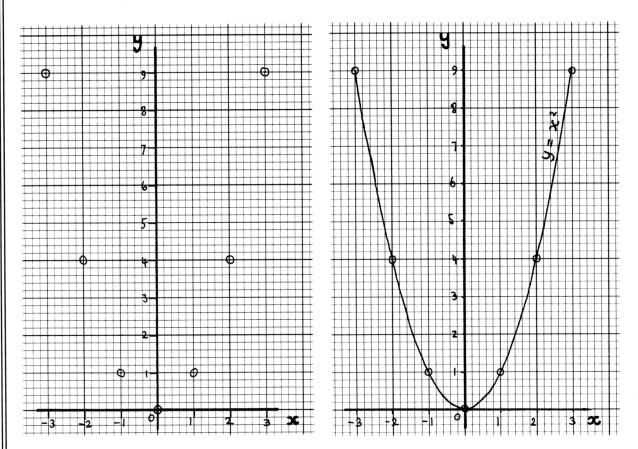

It is usually easier to draw a curve from <u>inside</u> the curve.

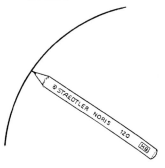

e.g. (2) Draw the graph of $y = x^2 - 4x + 3$, using values of x from −1 to +5.

x	−1	0	1	2	3	4	5
x^2	1	0	1	4	9	16	25
−4x	+4	0	−4	−8	−12	−16	−20
+3	+3	+3	+3	+3	+3	+3	+3
y	8	3	0	−1	0	3	8

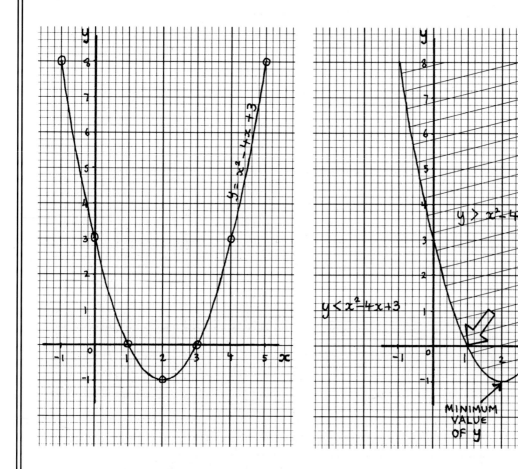

In the right-hand drawing, the striped area (inside the curve) contains all the values of y which are <u>greater than</u> $x^2 - 4x + 3$. The unstriped area (outside the curve) contains all the values of y which are <u>less than</u> $x^2 - 4x + 3$.

<u>Minimum value</u>

What is the minimum (lowest possible) value of $y = x^2 - 4x + 3$?

The lowest point on the graph is where $y = -1$.

The minimum value of y is −1.

The minimum value of $x^2 - 4x + 3$ is −1.

Some quadratic graphs have a MAXIMUM (highest possible) value.

Solution of quadratic equations

What is the solution of the quadratic equation $x^2 - 4x + 3 = 0$?

To find this, look at the points where the graph cuts the x axis (i.e. where y = 0), shown on the right-hand diagram (page 56) with arrows.

The x coordinate of each point is a solution.

The graph cuts the x axis at +1 and +3.

Solution of $x^2 - 4x + 3 = 0$ is <u>x = 1 or x = 3</u>.

Sometimes it is better to spread out the graph by making the units on the x axis twice the size, or more. This can prevent having a long thin graph which is squashed up, e.g.

$$y = x^2 - 4x + 3 \text{ could be drawn}$$

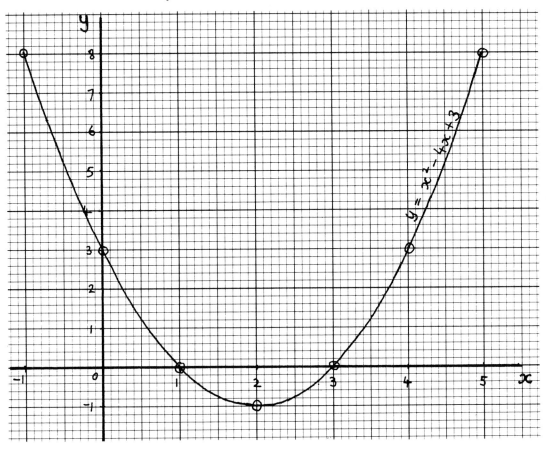

99 (a) To find points for the graph of $y = x^2 - 8$, copy and complete this table.

x	−4	−3	−2	−1	0	1	2	3	4
x^2	16		4						
−8	−8		−8						
y	8		−4						

(b) Plot the points from the completed table, e.g. (−4,8), (−2,−4), and join them with a curved line to give the graph of $y = x^2 - 8$.

100 (a) Make a table of values for the graph of $y = x^2 - 2x - 5$, using values of x from −3 to +5.

(b) Plot points and draw the graph of $y = x^2 - 2x - 5$.

(c) What is the minimum value of $x^2 - 2x - 5$?

101

(a) Make a table for the graph of y = 4x – x² + 3 with values of x –2, –1, 0, 1, 2, 3, 4, 5, 6.

(b) Draw an x axis from –2 to +6 with <u>2cm</u> representing 1 unit.
Draw a y axis from –9 to +7 with 1cm representing 1 unit.

(c) Draw the graph of y = 4x – x² + 3

(d) What is the maximum value of 4x – x² + 3 ?

(e) By finding the values of x at the points where the graph crosses the x axis, write down the two solutions of the equation 4x – x² + 3 = 0.

102

(a) Make a table for the graph of y = 7 – x² with values of x from –3 to +3 and then draw the graph.

(b) From your graph, find the solution to the quadratic equation 7 – x² = 0.

103

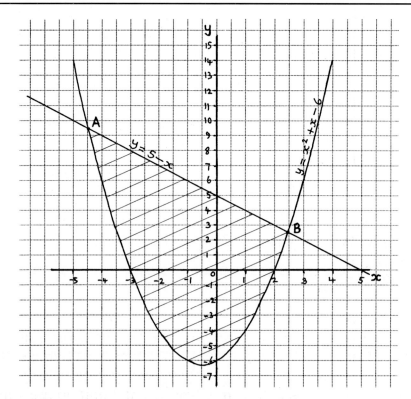

Look at the graphs and try these questions.

(a) What is the approximate minimum value of x² + x – 6 ?

(b) What value of x gives the minimum value of x² + x – 6 ?

(c) Find the two solutions of the quadratic equation x² + x – 6 = 0.

(d) Write down the approximate coordinates of the points A and B where y = 5 – x intersects y = x² + x – 6.

(e) Copy and complete 'The striped area contains the set of points where y is greater than.............. but less than...............

104

(a) Draw axes with x from –5 to +5 and y from 0 to +11.

(b) Draw the graph of y = x² – 4x + 6 for values of x from –1 to +5.

(c) What is the minimum value of x² – 4x + 6 ?

(d) Using the same axes, draw the graph of y = x + 3

(e) These graphs should intersect at two points. Write down the two values of x for which x² – 4x + 6 = x + 3.

(f) Shade the area in which the values of y are greater than x² – 4x + 6 but less than x + 3.

105

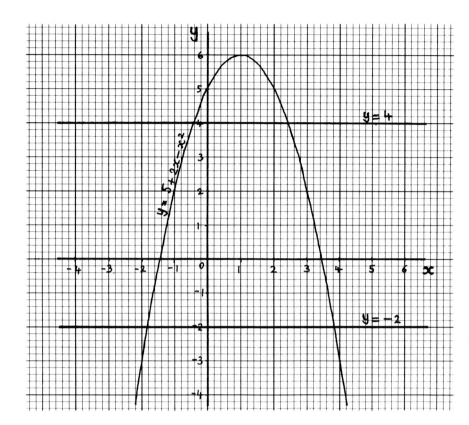

The drawing shows the graphs of $y = 5 + 2x - x^2$, $y = 4$ and $y = -2$.

(a) Use the graphs to find the approximate solutions to
   (i) $5 + 2x - x^2 = 0$
   (ii) $5 + 2x - x^2 = 4$
   (iii) $7 + 2x - x^2 = 0$ (Clue. Rearrange the equation.)

(b) What is the greatest possible value of $5 + 2x - x^2$?

(c) For what value of x is $5 + 2x - x^2$ at its greatest possible value ?

(d) By substituting in the equation, find the value of y when $x = 10$.

106 (a) Draw x and y axes with 1cm to represent 1 unit on the x axis and 1cm to represent 2 units on the y axis.

(b) Make a table for the graph of $y = x^2 + 3x - 5$ with values of x −6, −5, −4, −3, −2, −1, 0, 1, 2, 3.

(c) Draw the graph of $y = x^2 + 3x - 5$

(d) From the graph, find the solution to the equation $x^2 + 3x - 5 = 0$

(e) For what value of x is the graph at its minimum point ?

(f) At the minimum point, what is the value of y ?

107 (a) Draw axes for a graph.
   x axis from −4 to +4 with 2cm for each unit.
   y axis from −6 to +10 with 1cm for each unit.

(b) Draw the graph of $y = x^2 - 6$

(c) By noting where the graph cuts the x axis ($y = 0$), find the two solutions of the equation $x^2 - 6 = 0$.

(d) Using the same axes, draw the graph of $y = x^2 + 1$

(e) Explain why the equation $x^2 + 1 = 0$ cannot be solved by looking at the graph.

(f) Why is it impossible to solve $x^2 + 1 = 0$ by any method ?

108 (a) With 1cm to represent 1 unit, draw axes with x from –8 to +8, and y from 0 to +10.

(b) Mark the points F (0,4) and A (0,2).

(c) Plot points H (2,0), B (2, $2\frac{1}{2}$). Join FBH to make a triangle.

(d) Plot points J (4,0), C (4,4). Join FCJ to make a triangle.

(e) Plot points K (6,0), D ($6,6\frac{1}{2}$). Join FDK to make a triangle.

(f) Plot points L (8,0), E (8,10). Join FEL to make a triangle.

(g) Write down which special kind of triangle each of these is (Clue. FE = EL).

(h) Draw a smooth curve which passes exactly through points A, B, C, D and E. (Easier if you turn the graph upside down).

(i) Reflect the curve ABCDE in the y axis.

(j) Mark the curve : Graph of y = $\frac{x^2}{8}$ + 2

(k) Write next to the curve: The graph of $\frac{x^2}{8}$ + 2 is a PARABOLA with FOCUS (0,4) and DIRECTRIX y=0.

Five more graphs

(You will need an electronic calculator)

109 (a) Draw x and y axes from –4 to +4 each, with 2cm for 1 unit.

(b) Draw the graph of y = $\frac{1}{x}$ using the following values of x:

$-4, -3, -2, -1, -\frac{1}{2}, -\frac{1}{3}, -\frac{1}{4}, \frac{1}{4}, \frac{1}{3}, \frac{1}{2}, 1, 2, 3, 4.$

(c) Give a reason why this graph never touches the x or y axis.

110 (a) Draw an x axis from 0 to +3 with 4cm for 1 unit, and a y axis from –6 to +6 with 2cm for 1 unit.

(b) Draw the graph of y = $\frac{x^2}{\sqrt{x}}$ (the square of x divided by the square root of x) using values of x 0, $\frac{1}{2}$, 1, $1\frac{1}{2}$, 2, 3.

Remember that every positive number has TWO square roots, one positive (+) and one negative (–), e.g. $\sqrt{9}$= 3 and $\sqrt{9}$ = –3.

(c) Give a reason why x values of –1, –2, –3, etc., could not be used for this graph.

111 (a) Draw the graph of y = sin x (y = the sine of an angle of x degrees). Horizontal axis (x) –360° to +360° with 2cm to represent 90° Vertical axis (y) –1.0 to +1.0 with 8cm to represent 1.0

(b) Assuming you are using 20mm/2mm graph paper, what does one small square represent (i) on the x axis ?
(ii) on the y axis ?

(c) Using a calculator with a sin button (or a table with sine values), find the sine of each of the following values of x :
0°, 18°, 27°, 45°, 63°, 90°

(d) Plot the graph of y = sin x for values of x from 0° to 90°, joining the points with a neat curve.

(e) Find the sine of each of these x values:

$-360°, -270°, -180°, -90°, +180°, +270°, 360°$

From these results, complete the graph of $y = \sin x$ from $x=-360°$ to $x=+360°$. If you are not sure of the shape of the curve, find the sines of some other values of x between $-360°$ and $+360°$.

(f) From your graph find the value of
(i) the sine of angle 216°
(ii) the sine of angle 153°
(iii) the angles whose sine is 0.5

---

112 (a) Copy and complete this table of values for the graph of $y = x^3 - 6x$.

x	−3	−2	−1.4	−1	−0.5	0	0.5	1	1.4	2	3
x^3			−2.7						2.7		
$-6x$			+8.4						−8.4		
y			+5.7						−5.7		

(b) Draw the graph of $y = x^3 - 6x$. The points (−1.4, 5.7) and (1.4, −5.7) are the approximate maximum and minimum points on the graph between $x=-2$ and $x=+2$. These points give a clue about how to draw the graph.

(c) From the graph, find the three possible solutions of each of these equations.

(i) $x^3 - 6x = 0$
(ii) $x^3 - 6x + 4 = 0$

---

113 (a) Complete this table of values for the graph of $x^2 + y^2 = 36$

LINE 1	x	−6	$-5\frac{1}{2}$	−5	−4	−2	0	2	4	5	$5\frac{1}{2}$	6
LINE 2	36				36							
LINE 3	$-x^2$				−16							
LINE 4	y^2				20							
LINE 5	y				+4.5 or −4.5							

LINE 1 gives the value of x.
LINE 2 is always 36.
LINE 3 Work out the value of $-x^2$.
LINE 4 Work out $36 - x^2$. This gives y^2.
LINE 5 Find the square root of y^2. This gives y.

Remember. Every square (except 0) has TWO square roots, one positive (+) and one negative (−).

(b) Plot points from the x and y values in the table, e.g. (−4, 4.5) and (−4, −4.5), and draw the graph of $x^2 + y^2 = 36$.

(c) What is the shape of your completed graph ?

THREE-DIMENSIONAL COORDINATES

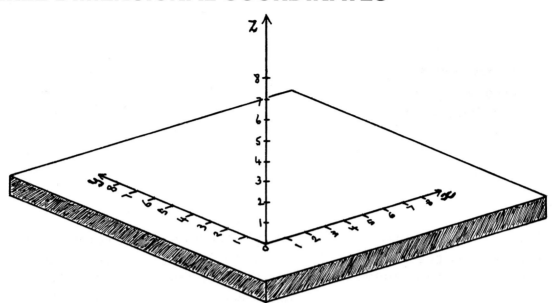

The axes and coordinates x and y are useful for finding the position of a point on a plane surface (flat surface), but for finding the position of a point in space, another axis and another coordinate are needed (**z axis and z coordinate).**

Look at the plan on page 2. The x and y axes start at the origin (0,0). The x axis goes towards the right of the page; the y axis goes away from you towards the top of the page.

Try to imagine another axis (z axis), also starting at the origin but coming straight up (vertically) out of the page.

Pretend that all the places in the plan are on level ground. Also pretend that a helicopter is hovering in the air 3 units directly above The Tower. The coordinates of The Tower are (8,6), so the coordinates of the helicopter would be (8,6,3).

Three-dimensional coordinates are written (x,y,z).

The z axis is at right angles to the x axis, and also at right angles to the y axis.

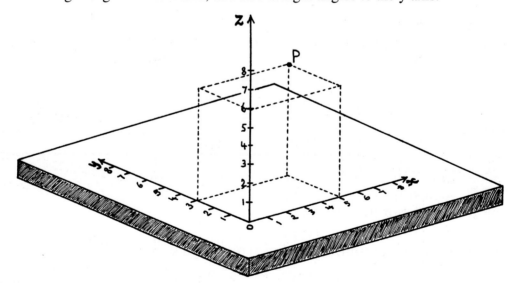

To find the position of P in the diagram above, count from the origin (0,0,0) along the x axis 5 units, along the y axis 3 units, up the z axis 6 units.

The coordinates of P are (5,3,6).

It can be helpful to draw, or imagine, a cuboid (box shape). The point you are identifying is at the corner furthest away from the origin.

114

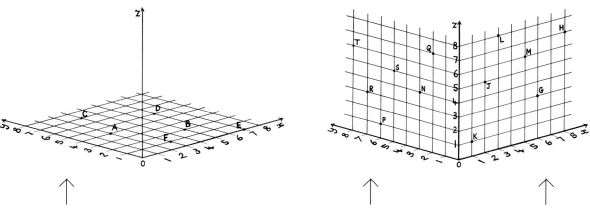

For all points on this plane (flat surface), the z coordinate is zero (0), e.g. the coordinates of A are (2,4,0).

For all points on this plane, the x coordinate is zero, e.g. N is (0,3,4).

For all points on this plane, the y coordinate is zero, e.g. G is (6,0,3).

Write down the coordinates of each of B, C, D, E, F, H, J, K, L, M, P, Q, R, S and T.

115

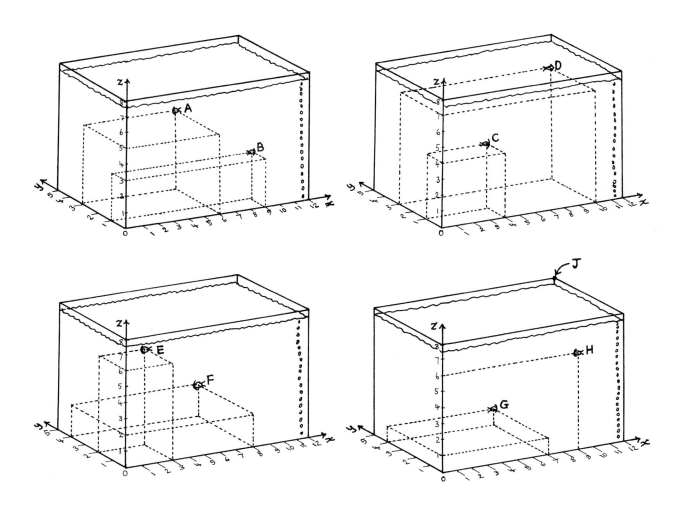

(i) Find the coordinates of each of the fishes A, B, C, D, E, F, G and H.

(ii) What are the coordinates of the far top corner (J) of the fish tank?

116

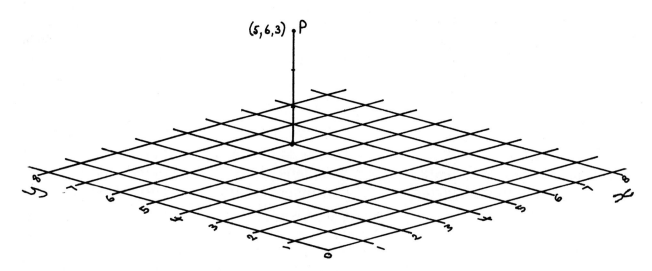

The diagram shows a grid with x and y axes. On this grid there is a pole whose top P has coordinates (5,6,3). The bottom of the pole has coordinates (5,6,0).

(a) Photocopy the diagram, or trace it on to plain paper.

(b) On your copy, mark the point (6,2,0) on the grid. This point is the bottom of a vertical pole whose top (A) has coordinates (6,2,3). Draw the pole, using 1cm for each unit. Your pole should be 3cm tall. Mark the top of the pole with letter A.

(c) Using 1cm for each unit, draw a vertical pole whose top B has coordinates (1,4,7). (Clues. What are the coordinates of the bottom of the pole? How high is the pole?)

(d) Using 1cm for each unit, draw vertical poles with these tops:–
C (3,1,6); D (2,8,1); E (7,2,4); F (0,0,9); G (3,5,2); H (7,0,2); J (0,5,4); K (5,5,5).

117

In the diagram,
positive (+) x represents East,
positive (+) y represents North,
positive (+) z represents Up.

(a) What do these represent?
(i) negative (–) x
(ii) negative (–) y
(iii) negative (–) z

(b) Paul stands at point P (2,–2,0).
What are the coordinates of the point where Paul ends up if he starts at P and walks

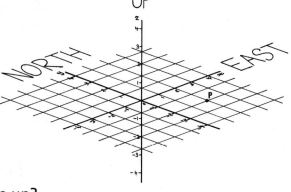

(i) 5 units North and 1 unit East?
(ii) 3 units North and 5 units West?
(iii) 1 unit South, 2 units East and 3 units up?
(iv) 4 units North, 2 units West and 1 unit down?
(v) 6 units West, 1 unit South and 4 units down?